ELECTRIC COOPERATIVES:
ON THE THRESHOLD OF A NEW ERA

PUBLIC UTILITIES REPORTS, INC.

Vienna, Virginia
1996

First Printing, January 1996

Library of Congress Catalog Card No. 95-73051

ISBN 0-910325-63-4

Printed in the United States of America

TABLE OF CONTENTS

PART 5

PREFACE

That the electric utility industry is undergoing great change in the mid-1990s is not news to anyone reading the business press or a local newspaper. Merger activity among electric utilities has escalated. Federal and state regulators have announced their support for competitive power markets. Utility companies are establishing offices in service territories other than their own with the expectation of establishing a customer base in competitors' franchise areas.

While much of the attention has focused on activity within the investor-owned segment, electric cooperatives play a significant role in the delivery of power throughout the United States. As such, they are not unaffected by the tremendous changes taking place in the generation and transmission business. Distribution cooperatives find their relationships with customers and power suppliers shaped by new economic forces. Founded on the premise that the interests of the consumer-members are the ultimate priority, cooperatives will focus considerable attention on the issue of customer choice.

The literature on public utilities continues to expand. While many publications address the issues of regulation (or deregulation), financing, and competition in the utility industry, we found none that focused discussion on the unique structure and mission of electric cooperatives.

The purpose of the book is to examine, in basic terms, how the electric cooperative segment of the electric utility industry operates, how it developed and is structured, and what are some of its most pressing challenges today. In our effort to make sections of the book as self-contained as possible, some explanations may have been repeated rather than referring the reader to another section of the text. Some industry specialists may finds portions of the text elementary. Our objective is to be as clear and inclusive as possible for those who may be working within the cooperative system as well as for those readers for whom this is their first introduction. We trust that our veterans of the cooperative industry will skip over the offending section and go on to the material that will help them.

The book is divided into five parts plus appendices and an index.

Part One, *The Cooperative Organization*, describes the origins and structure of electric cooperatives and offers a chronology of the legislation that gave rise to the development of specialized cooperative organizations.

Part Two, *Generation and Distribution of Power*, describes the physical laws and engineering techniques involved in the production and distribution of electricity, outlines the role of the federal government in power generation, and introduces some of the new players in the electricity generation business.

Part Three, *Accounting and Finance*, discusses the financial and accounting procedures so vital to electric cooperatives and explores the various loan programs available to them. In addition, the issue of supplemental financing and the role of the private capital markets is explained.

Part Four, *Regulation and Rates*, takes a look at the Rural Utilities Service as regulator, outlines some basic rate structures, and identifies the significant pieces of federal legislation which have had an impact on the operations of electric cooperatives.

Part Five, *Competitive Strategies*, offers examples of the challenges electric cooperatives face as the entire electric utility industry is transformed by the forces of deregulation and competition.

The appendices provide additional information. The *Table of Acronyms* is an invaluable guide to the many organizations which are part of the electric cooperative industry. The *Glossary* highlights those terms most important to the understanding of the operations and financing of co-ops. The *List of Cooperatives* is intended to give the reader a sense of the number, size and location of the many electric cooperatives operating throughout the United States. They are identified as being either distribution cooperatives, G&Ts, or special cooperative organizations. A *Subject Index* follows the appendices.

The text of the book is the result of the collaborative efforts of several dedicated and knowledgeable individuals. Patricia Lloyd Williams transformed the genesis of the idea for the book into a complete and cohesive text. Her thorough research and attention to detail are evident throughout. John Vanvig assisted in the review of the text, contributing the insight gleaned through his many years as writer and editor at the National Rural Electric Cooperative Association. Ira Shesser, drawing upon his long time involvement with the industry—as a legislative staff member of the Rural Electrification Administration, legislative research coordinator for NRECA, as first loan officer at the Cooperative Finance Corporation and later assistant to the governor—carefully checked the accuracy of details and interpretation of legislation.

At PUR, Lorraine Howard edited, checked, supervised, and ushered the book through the publication process. Yvonne Patrick and Jamie Simon assisted in the compilation of the appendices. Their efforts are greatly appreciated.

Thanks also to John B. Bruce of the Virginia Maryland Delaware Association of Electric Cooperatives who provided us with the photograph for the cover of this book.

Susan M. Johnson
Publisher
Public Utilities Reports, Inc.
December 1995

PART 1

THE COOPERATIVE ORGANIZATION

CHAPTER 1

THE EVOLUTION OF ELECTRIC COOPERATIVES

In 1935, the United States had 6.8 million farms. Less than 750,000 of them had access to central station electric service. Those that did frequently paid a large fee to get the service, and they also paid higher rates than consumers in the towns and cities, where virtually 100 percent of the population had access to electricity. People living in cities enjoyed amenities and standard of living that could not be achieved in rural areas. As a result, significant numbers of people were moving from the farms to the cities, seeking better jobs and an improved quality of life. Agriculture remained an important part of the national economy, however, and this population migration was a cause for increasing concern.

As president, Franklin D. Roosevelt launched a wide range of programs which used public funds to finance public works as part of his New Deal to end the Depression. On May 11, 1935, he established the Rural Electrification Administration (REA) by Executive Order 7037 under the authority of the Emergency Relief Appropriation Act of 1935. REA was established as an independent lending agency with the passage of the Rural Electrification Act of 1936.

REA's goal was to electrify rural America, and it quickly became apparent that the best way to do this was to work with the rural Americans themselves. With the financial support and technical assistance of REA, rural people organized a network of electric cooperatives to organize, build, and operate electric utility systems in their own communities.

Rural electrification became one of the great success stories of the New Deal, and today, there are almost 1,000 rural electric cooperatives providing service to more than 30 million people in 46 states.

WHAT IS A COOPERATIVE?

Webster's Dictionary defines cooperative as "marked by a willingness and ability to work with others." But since 1883 Webster has offered an additional meaning: "an enterprise or organization owned by and operated for the benefit of those using its services." We're interested in the second definition—the cooperative as an organization engaged in significant economic activity. According to the National Cooperative Business Association, more than 100 million people are

members of 47,000 cooperatives throughout the United States. There are pro-
ducer-owned cooperatives which help farmers and small businesses market their
goods, (i.e., Land O'Lakes, Service Star, and Blue Diamond Corporation) worker-
owned cooperatives which own and operate commercial and industrial businesses,
and consumer-owned cooperatives which provide consumers with products and
services as diverse as food, insurance, child care, and electricity. Cooperatives provide almost any type of goods or services provided by other types of business
organizations.

The birth of the modern consumer cooperative movement is traced to Rochdale,
England, and the organization of the Rochdale Society of Equitable Pioneers in
1844. Although cooperatives were organized before that—Benjamin Franklin
organized the first successful cooperative in the United States, the Philadelphia
Contributionship for the Insurances of Houses from Loss by Fire, in 1752—the
Rochdale cooperative developed the organizational principles and practices followed by most cooperatives today:

- open membership with no political or religious discrimination

- democratic control on a one-member, one-vote basis

- return of net earnings to members proportionally to their patronage
  of the business

- education of members

- cooperation with other cooperatives

Part I of this guide to electric cooperatives will highlight the general structure of
cooperatives, their special niche in the American economy, and some of the legislation that has shaped their evolution.

PUBLIC UTILITIES AND THE AMERICAN ECONOMY

The term "public utility" usually refers to a group of businesses that supply services vital to society and that have been subjected to some type of regulation over
their rates and service practices. In return, they have been shielded from some
types of competition. Some public utilities are owned by private individuals, some
by government bodies, and some, like electric cooperatives, are owned by their
customers. While some people use the term public utility synonymously with
investor-owned utility, it actually refers to the nature of the business, not to its
ownership or operation.

Public utilities can be divided into two major classes. One type supplies continuous or repeated service to its customers through a permanent physical connection
to the customer. Electric cooperatives provide that type of service, as do companies which supply natural gas, water and wastewater services, steam heat, and
telecommunications services. The second type of public utility provides transportation services and includes bus companies, motor freight carriers, gas and oil
pipelines, railroads, taxicabs, subways, and ship and barge lines.

Electric cooperatives, like other public utilities, occupy a special niche in the U.S. economy. That economy is based on **capitalism**, a system in which the resources for the production and distribution of goods and services are privately owned and operated for profit. Capitalism relies on the free market to allocate limited resources and enjoys relative freedom from governmental restraint. Competition determines what goods are produced, who gets them, and at what price.

A **monopoly** exists when there is no competition, and only one seller supplies many buyers. (An oligopoly exists when only a few sellers affect, but do not control, the market.) U.S. commercial law forbids most monopolies because, in the absence of competition, the monopolist is in a position to set prices by controlling the supply of a product or service, leaving consumers at the supplier's mercy.

Public utilities, however, have generally been viewed as **natural monopolies**, or businesses whose costs of production are so high and economies of scale so great that one firm can offer the product or service cheaper than two or more competing firms. Competition in providing electric service, for example, has historically been viewed as uneconomic because of the potential for costly and unnecessary duplication of power plants, transmission and distribution lines, substations, and transformers. Recently, many observers have come to believe that the generation of electricity is no longer a monopoly function. State and federal regulatory changes aimed at fostering a competitive market for wholesale electric power are taking place.

Several characteristics of electric utilities distinguish them from other types of businesses. First, electric utilities have historically enjoyed benefits from economies of scale: that is, the larger the size and higher the output of the utility plant, the lower the cost of production and distribution per unit, or kilowatt-hour, sold. To achieve the most efficient operation of a high cost generation, transmission and distribution system, therefore, required that the supplier have a monopoly on service. Second, the utility market is limited by the necessary physical connection of electric lines between the utility plant and the consumer. It has not been practical to store electricity or to transport it over long distances.

Third, the electric power industry is **capital intensive**—that is, it requires lots of money and access to credit to produce and deliver service. Electric utilities require greater initial and continuing financial investments in facilities to produce their product than do most other businesses. Cooperative distribution systems, for example, have invested about $2 in facilities for every dollar they collect in revenue. Generation and transmission cooperatives have invested more than $3.50 in plant and facilities for each dollar of revenue they collect. In contrast, many large manufacturing enterprises average less than 50 cents of investment for each $1 of revenue. **Fixed costs**, such as generating plants, poles, wires, and substations, do not vary with the amount of electricity produced. They represent a larger proportion of the cost of producing and delivering electricity than **variable costs**. The variable costs, such as fuel and salaries, are directly related to the amount of product produced. To cover their large fixed costs, utilities rely more heavily on debt financing than do most other types of businesses. And because

---

**WILL PUBLIC UTILITIES CONTINUE TO BE
NATURAL MONOPOLIES?**

The idea that electric utilities must function as natural monopolies has become a matter of great debate in the 1990s. "Competition in the whole-sale generation sector has brought about the demise of the vertical monopoly as the sole legitimate model for the utility. Other elements of the 'natural' monopoly, such as transmission and distribution, may also prove vulnerable in light of technological change and global competitive economic forces that give customers increasing choices to leverage utility services."

SOURCE: *O'Connor, P.R., Barnich, T.L., and Clausen, C.M., "Progressive Choice," The Electric Industry in Transition, Public Utilities Reports, Inc., 1994.*

---

of their special characteristics, electric cooperatives often rely more heavily on debt than do other types of utilities.

Public utilities are also different from other businesses in that they are required by law to serve all willing and able buyers. They must estimate the demand for their services, often years in advance, and plan construction programs to meet that demand. Electric utilities must be able to produce and deliver their product on demand, since storage of significant amounts of electricity is not yet feasible. The utility must either have sufficient reserve capacity to meet demand or have access to other sources of power for its customers.

A final difference between public utilities and other types of businesses is the way in which prices, or rates, are set. Utility rates are approved by a regulatory body, usually after lengthy consideration of many factors. For most electric cooperatives, the board of directors of the co-op sets rates, although some co-ops are regulated by state or federal commissions. Most utilities, including cooperatives, offer a variety of rates, depending on when electricity is used, what it is used for, and who uses it. Such **price discrimination** allows the utility to recover the widely divergent costs of serving different types of customers. How rates should be set in the future—through continued regulation, a competitive market, or some combination of the two—is the subject of much debate in the changing electric utility industry and will be addressed in later chapters.

THE STRUCTURE OF ELECTRIC COOPERATIVES

The most basic difference between an electric cooperative and an investor-owned utility is ownership: electric cooperatives are owned by those they serve. As a result, cooperatives can be very responsive to the needs of their consumer-members and their local communities. Any individual or business within a co-op's service territory becomes a member-owner by joining the cooperative and buying electricity from it. The rights and responsibilities of membership are set forth in the cooperative's bylaws, which are adopted by the members and may be amended by them from time to time. Members participate in the operation of the co-op by electing the board of directors. Each member has one vote.

In contrast, an investor-owned utility is owned by its stockholders, and voting privileges are based on the number of shares of stock owned. Municipal utilities are owned by the public, too, but they are overseen by local government entities.

The co-op's board of directors is responsible for establishing the cooperative's basic policies, goals and strategies. The board hires a manager to carry out those policies and strategies. The manager is responsible for the day-to-day operations of the cooperative, including staffing, and develops and executes plans to achieve the board's objectives. The board is then responsible for reviewing management's performance and ensuring that its objectives are being met. The directors usually serve without pay other than reimbursement of expenses. Thus, in a co-op, the manager reports to the board of directors and the directors, in turn, are accountable to the members.

Members of electric cooperatives are generally not required to make direct financial investments in the organization, other than a membership fee. The bylaws usually stipulate that the fee will be returned when the member leaves the cooperative.

Since they are owned by their customers, electric cooperatives do not operate for profit. As nonprofit organizations, cooperatives do not pay income taxes on their electricity revenues. They do, however, pay the other types of taxes that utilities are required to pay. Any net margin of revenue over expenses is credited to members in proportion to their usage of electricity in the form of capital credits, or **patronage capital**. No interest is paid on this form of investment, but cooperatives are required to return this capital to their members. Size of margins and the timing of capital returns are key decisions for the board.

Cooperative business principles require electric co-ops to set aside specific funds for educational programs which may include newsletters, seminars or youth programs. For example, the Electric Cooperatives of South Carolina, the statewide lobbying and service organization, has used educational funds to develop a program to educate the public, including state and local officials and new members, about cooperatives. The basic message is that cooperatives do pay taxes and contribute to the community.

Each cooperative is required to hold an annual meeting to elect board members and conduct other cooperative business. This also provides an opportunity for members to learn more about cooperative activities from the management and board of directors of the cooperative.

OTHER CORPORATE STRUCTURES

Many electric cooperatives have contractual or other relationships with **investor-owned utilities**. Like electric cooperatives, investor-owned utilities may generate, transmit, and distribute electric energy. The corporate structure of an investor-owned utility, however, is very different from that of a cooperative. Investor-owned utilities (IOUs), or privately owned utilities, are owned by shareholders who invest private funds in the company. The shareholders are not required to live in the service territory of the utility or purchase power from it. Investor-owned utilities own about 77 percent of the generating capacity in the United States.

Publicly-owned utilities are nonprofit organizations supported by the consumers directly served by that utility within a given political or governmental jurisdiction. There are several types of public ownership of utilities including ownership by municipalities, cities, counties, states, and the federal government. There are also public utility districts, which are independent of city and county government. Similar to a school district or a water district, a public utility district is a form of local tax-supported organization, voted into existence by the majority of residents of a given area for the specific purpose of rendering a utility service. State law usually provides the authority for the creation of such a district.

While cooperatives are technically not publicly-owned utilities, they are classed by rating agencies with publicly-owned utilities under the broad category of public power.

FIGURE 1.1. U.S. Installed Generating Capacity

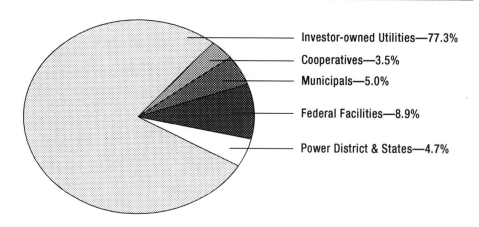

In 1993 Electric Cooperatives owned a small but significant portion of the nation's generating capacity.

SOURCE: *Statistical Yearbook of the Electric Utility Industry, Edison Electric Institute, 1993 Edition.*

TYPES OF ELECTRIC COOPERATIVES

There are three basic functions related to providing electricity:

- generation, the actual production of electricity

- transmission, moving it from where it is generated to the general area where it will be used

- distribution, actually delivering it to the end-user

An investor-owned utility typically performs all three of these functions, although strong competition is emerging in generation and efforts are under way, especially by large consumers, to restructure the other functions. The cooperative segment of the industry approaches electric service in a different way.

FIGURE 1.2. U.S. Electric Utilities

Type of Utility	Number
Wholesale Generating Companies	19
Service Companies	13
Investor-Owned Utilities	193
Municipal Systems	1,818
Rural Cooperatives	920
Public Power Districts	73
Irrigation Districts	9
U.S. Government Systems	36
State Systems	68

SOURCE: *Electrical World Directory of Electric Utilities, McGraw-Hill, 1996 Edition*

Distribution Systems

The first electric cooperatives created were **distribution systems** organized to provide power to their consumer-member-owners. In most cases, the distribution system purchases power at wholesale for re-sale to its members. A few distribution systems also have generation and transmission facilities. About 90 percent of those served by electric cooperatives are residential consumers, including farms. The report of the REA Administrator for fiscal year 1993 noted that 872 distribution borrowers were providing service to more than 12.9 million members—the equivalent of more than 30 million users—in 46 states, Puerto Rico, and the Virgin Islands.

FIGURE 1.3. Rural Electric Borrowers

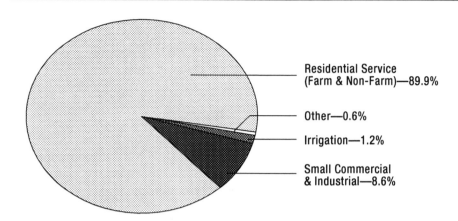

Residential Service
(Farm & Non-Farm)—89.9%

Other—0.6%

Irrigation—1.2%

Small Commercial
& Industrial—8.6%

SOURCE: *1994 Statistical Report Rural Electric Borrowers, U.S. Department of Agriculture, Rural Utilities Service, 1995.*

Generation and Transmission Cooperatives

As the needs of their membership grew, many distribution systems began to face problems in getting adequate supplies of reasonably priced bulk power. The co-ops were frequently saddled with excessively high wholesale rates, poor service, and severe contract restrictions as their wholesale suppliers came to see the co-ops as competitors for attractive loads.

Many distribution co-ops banded together to form **generation and transmission cooperatives (G&Ts)**. Later, in a few cases, groups of G&Ts joined together to form "super G&Ts." The G&Ts generate or purchase wholesale power for sale to their member systems. They also provide or purchase transmission capacity to deliver the power to the distribution network. The formation of G&Ts allowed member systems to gain the benefits of sharing larger, more economical power plants while retaining the advantages of local ownership, control and operation. Distribution systems are bound to their G&Ts by the "all-requirements" contract, under which the distribution system agrees to purchase—and the G&T agrees to provide—all of the distribution co-op's power needs. The distribution system agrees to pay rates sufficient to cover all of the G&T's costs. By guaranteeing the G&T a sufficient revenue stream, the all-requirements contract provides the primary security for nearly all G&T borrowings. In 1994, there were 61 operating generation and transmission cooperatives providing power to more than 700 distribution co-ops throughout the U.S.

The first federal loans for generation and transmission were made in 1936 to two separate utilities, Federated Electric and Central Federated Electric in Iowa. The co-ops installed diesel plants and delivered power over distribution lines to their member systems. The two systems later merged to form Corn Belt Power Cooperative and built one of the first steam plants constructed by electric cooperatives.

G&T cooperatives obtain power for their member systems from a variety of sources. In addition to their own plants, they purchase capacity and energy from other power generators, including other G&Ts and the federal power marketing administrations, such as the Western Area Power Administration. A number of G&Ts organized in the 1960s and 1970s obtained their initial generating capacity through joint participation projects with investor-owned utilities.

The government restricted G&T power plant construction loans to situations in which no other power sources were available or in which a G&T could provide a substantially lower cost of power than other power suppliers. In a number of cases, an alternate power supplier, often an investor-owned utility, offered reduced rates to keep distribution systems from forming a G&T. The G&T option thus provided a valuable cost yardstick which provided benefits to distribution systems, even when a G&T was not organized.

Statewide Organizations

The electric cooperatives, working together, have created statewide organizations that provide many services to members. The statewide organizations coordinate legislative activities and provide job training and safety programs, communication and educational programs, as well as support for individual systems' member services programs.

Service Organizations

Additional cooperatives have been organized to provide special services to distribution and G&T systems. Data processing cooperatives provide computer services to their member systems. Materials supply cooperatives provide the benefits of joint purchasing of construction materials such as poles, line, transformers and other electrical components. Some co-ops also sponsor credit unions, another form of cooperative, to provide financial services to their members.

CHAPTER

A BRIEF HISTORY OF THE RURAL ELECTRIFICATION ADMINISTRATION: BACKBONE OF THE ELECTRIC COOPERATIVE PROGRAM

As noted in Chapter 1, in 1935 less than 750,000 of the 6.8 million farms in the U.S. had access to **central station electric service**. Those that did paid huge fees to cover the power company's investment in facilities to serve them and also paid higher power costs than electric consumers in urban areas, where almost everyone had access to electricity.

Investor-owned utilities showed little interest in expanding their lines to serve rural consumers where low population density meant greater distances between service points—and thus higher costs and lower revenues. Few electric executives recognized the potential for new agricultural uses of electricity. The common wisdom was that farmers would not know how to use electricity if they had it and couldn't pay for it even if they did.

As governor of New York, Franklin D. Roosevelt established the New York Power Authority, which conducted some of the first extensive technical studies on the cost of providing power to various types of consumers. So when Roosevelt became president, he was well-informed on the issues surrounding rural electrification— including studies showing that electricity had the potential to significantly increase farm productivity as well as to ease the backbreaking labor of farm life.

As president, Roosevelt launched a wide range of programs which used public funds to finance public works as part of his New Deal to end the Depression. On May 11, 1935, he established the **Rural Electrification Administration (REA)** by Executive Order 7037 under the authority of the Emergency Relief Appropriation Act of 1935.

Morris L. Cooke, an engineer and advisor on rural electrification issues to Roosevelt's Secretary of Interior Harold Ickes, was named REA's first Administrator. Initially, REA was a part of Roosevelt's overall effort to provide jobs and unemployment relief. It soon became apparent that developing electric systems required specialized engineering and management skills and that rural electrification required a more extensive effort than could be provided under the emergency relief program.

"In this period of stress and shifting standards in American life, one master problem stands out. This is rural rehabilitation. But of course the problem can be made to sound more simple than it really is. In any plan for rehabilitating American agriculture, one must include the salvation of our soils from erosion, the building up of farm incomes and a general improvement in the levels of living to the end that the gap which now exists between urban and country life may be closed. And in any such planning for the economic and cultural betterment of life in rural America, electrification must play an increasingly important part."

—Radio Address by Morris L. Cooke
First Administrator of the Rural Electrification Administration
October 21, 1935

REA was established as an independent lending agency with the passage of the Rural Electrification Act of 1936 (REA later became a part of the U.S. Department of Agriculture).

FIGURE 2.1. The Rural Electrification Act of 1936

- authorized the REA Administrator to make loans for rural electrification and for facilities and activities necessary to provide electric energy to people in rural areas who were not receiving central station electric service.

- specifically authorized the REA Administrator to make loans for the construction and operation of generating plants, electric transmission and distribution lines, or systems for furnishing electric energy.

- authorized the REA Administrator to make loans to finance wiring installations and electric and plumbing appliances and equipment.

- defined a rural area as "any area of the United States not included within the boundaries of any city, village or borough having a population in excess of fifteen hundred inhabitants" and included both farm and nonfarm businesses and residents. The definition has been interpreted to allow REA borrowers to continue to obtain loans to serve population growth and areas annexed by municipalities in areas originally meeting the guideline.

- gave preference for loans to municipalities, public utility districts, and cooperatives, although loans to other types of organizations, including investor-owned utilities, were permitted.

REA FOSTERS COOPERATIVE CONCEPT

REA's early efforts focused on encouraging the investor-owned utilities to extend their lines to provide service in rural areas. It was only after that effort failed that REA began to concentrate on achieving its goals through electric cooperatives. A few electric cooperatives had been organized either as independent organizations or as agencies to distribute power offered by the Tennessee Valley Authority under legislation enacted in 1933. It quickly became apparent that this form of organization offered many advantages in supplying power to rural areas. Farmers throughout the nation were familiar with cooperative concepts and had successfully organized co-ops for such diverse purposes as purchasing, marketing, and irrigating. These types of cooperatives, however, did not require the large amounts of capital or technical expertise needed to provide electric service.

COOPERATIVES HAVE A BIG IMPACT

Cooperatives come in all sizes, from small buying clubs to businesses included in the *Fortune 500*. Many cooperatives are household names—Welch's, Land O'Lakes, Ocean Spray, Sunkist, Publix Supermarkets, ACE Hardware, Nationwide Insurance, and the Associated Press. Furthermore:

- About thirty percent of farmers' products and farm supplies in the U.S. are marketed through cooperatives.

- Rural electric cooperatives operate more than half of the electric distribution lines in the United States and provide electricity for 30 million people.

- Over 50 million Americans are served by insurance companies owned by or closely affiliated with cooperatives.

- Food cooperatives have been innovators in the marketplace in the areas of unit pricing, consumer protection, and nutritional labeling.

- Retailer-owned food and hardware cooperatives make it possible for hundreds of independent store owners to successfully compete with large chains.

- Child care and nursery school cooperatives serve more than 50,000 families.

- There are approximately one million cooperative housing units serving households with a range of income levels and housing needs.

- Credit unions have over 67 million members and assets in excess of $100 billion.

- The Farm Credit System has 500,000 borrowers with a loan volume of $53.9 billion.

SOURCE: *National Cooperative Business Association, 1994*

The rural electric program was successful because REA was able to provide both of those key elements. It was authorized by Congress to provide significant amounts of capital for rural electrification. Beyond that, and equally important, REA provided the technical support that inexperienced rural people needed to organize, build and operate electric utility systems. REA attorneys addressed the legal issues involved and drafted model legislation for states to authorize the incorporation of the new cooperatives. REA field representatives assisted local leaders in organizing the cooperatives and recruiting members.

Where investor-owned utility engineers had approached rural service areas with the same techniques used in cities, REA engineers lowered rural construction costs by developing simplified standardized designs. They eliminated the crossbars on distribution poles and increased the span between poles to reduce the cost of materials. They applied mass production techniques to construction and further reduced building and labor costs. They developed standards and specifications for construction, equipment, and materials.

Such standardization also provided a benefit to operations. A cooperative suffering widespread outages as the result of an ice storm or hurricane could get help from another co-op's crews, who would be familiar with its construction and operations.

REA also developed accounting procedures and provided management support. Finally, REA offered programs to teach people how to use electricity and, through the local cooperatives, provided loan funds to finance consumer wiring, irrigation, and equipment investments.

This specialized assistance and support was of great benefit to the cooperatives and the rural residents served by them. It also protected the government's investment by creating strong systems which would be able to repay their loans. By 1940, just five years after REA was created, the percentage of farms with electric service jumped from 11 percent to 30.4 percent. By 1953, more than 90 percent of U.S. farms had electricity. Today, central station electricity is available to more than 99 percent of the nation's rural residents. Because of REA's loan programs and activities, people living in rural areas have the same access to electricity and telecommunications services as those who live in urban areas.

The success of the electrification program focused attention on other rural needs. On October 28, 1949, the REAct was amended to authorize REA to make loans to furnish and improve rural telephone service. At that time, only 36 percent of farms had telephone service of some type, and it was often unreliable. Even with the help of REA, it was not until 1975 that 90 percent of U.S. farms had telephone service. REA loans were also used to upgrade existing service and extend one-party service to more than 90 percent of the telephone borrowers' subscribers.

FIGURE 2.2. Percentage of Farms with Electric and Telephone Service
(U.S. Totals)

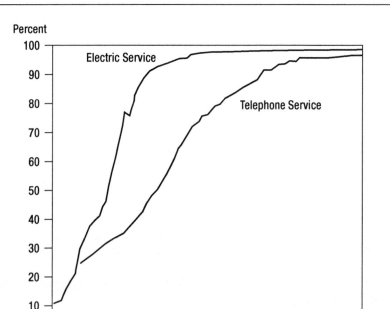

SOURCE: *A Brief History of the Rural Electric and Telephone Programs, U.S. Department of Agriculture, Rural Electrification Administration, 1988.*

The Advent of Supplemental Financing

By the 1960s, it was clear that the capital needs of rural electric systems were becoming so large that REA would not be able to meet the program's capital requirements without a substantial increase in government lending. After an unsuccessful attempt in 1966-67 to establish a federally-supported rural electric bank, the rural electric systems established the National Rural Utilities Cooperative Finance Corporation (CFC) to provide additional funding. A not-for-profit cooperative self-help financing institution, CFC was organized in 1969 to act as a conduit between the electric systems and the private capital markets. REA established a policy of requiring supplemental loans from lenders other than REA as a condition for almost all of its loans. Subsequent to the organization of CFC, the Banks for Cooperatives, an arm of the Farm Credit System, also began to provide loans to rural electric systems. CFC and other supplemental lenders will be discussed in further detail later in this chapter.

Telephone borrowers were successful in establishing the Rural Telephone Bank (RTB) in 1971 to provide additional funds for their needs. The federal government provided the initial capitalization for RTB.

Congress Gives REA Guarantee Authority

Congress mandated major changes in the rural electric program in 1973. On December 29, 1972, the Nixon Administration issued a directive placing the REA loan program under the authority of the Consolidated Farm and Rural Development Act as amended by the Rural Development Act of 1972, effective January 1, 1973. The change would have eliminated the traditional REA loan program, replacing it with insured and guaranteed loans from private sources. Other provisions included charges for guarantees, limitations on loan amounts, and certification requirements. The purpose of the change in the loan program was to eliminate the impact of the REA program on the federal budget.

The action precipitated a crisis in the rural electric program. Despite its stated purpose, the action was perceived by many to be a direct attempt to eliminate the rural electric program. As a result of the action, REA was unable to make loans between January 1, 1973 and April 17, 1973, when new administrative procedures were put into place. Most rural electric systems chose not to pursue financing under the new program.

The issue was resolved with legislation enacted on May 11, 1973. The new legislation amended the REAct to replace the two percent direct loan program with insured and guaranteed loans while maintaining the authority of the Administrator within the provisions of the REAct. The new program provided insured loans at a five percent interest rate with special hardship loans at a two percent interest rate for systems with low consumer densities or low average revenues per mile of line. A Rural Electrification and Telephone Revolving Fund was established to provide the loans. The Revolving Fund obtained funds by selling its loan notes to private investors. REA insured the payment of the notes. The legislation also provided for a loan guarantee program under which REA would guarantee the repayment of loans made at market rates by private lenders.

In an unrelated action, the Federal Financing Bank (FFB) was established on December 28, 1973 to coordinate federal and federally assisted borrowings. REA entered into a loan commitment agreement with FFB on August 14, 1974, and FFB provided funding for the REA guaranteed loans.

The original concept behind the Rural Electrification Act was to improve the quality of life in rural areas, and whatever other changes occurred, that remained the central purpose of the program.

FIGURE 2.3. Congress Steps In

These are among the most significant legislative actions affecting the rural electric program.

- Emergency Relief Appropriation Act of 1935
  - Gave President Roosevelt the authorities which enabled him to create the Rural Electrification Administration by Executive Order 7037, issued May 11, 1935.

- Rural Electrification Act of 1936
  - Established REA as independent lending agency with 10-year life and authorized REA to make loans for rural electrification.

- The Pace Act of 1944
  - Established REA as a permanent agency, fixed the interest rate on loans at 2 percent, extended repayment period to 35 years—instead of 25—and required area coverage, or full service, within a territory.

- 1949 amendments to the REAct authorized loans for the purpose of furnishing and improving rural telephone service.

- A major 1973 amendment to the REAct made basic changes in the REA loan program
  - Replaced the direct 2 percent loan program with insured loans at a standard 5 percent interest rate (with special hardship loans at 2 percent).
  - Established a revolving fund to provide the loans.
  - Authorized REA to guarantee loans made by other lenders.

- Federal Financing Bank established in 1973 to coordinate federal and federally assisted borrowings.

- Department of Energy Organization Act of 1977
  - Required REA to consider criteria established by the Secretary of Energy in making or guaranteeing loans for generation or transmission purposes.

- Omnibus Budget Reconciliation Act of 1986
  - Authorized the prepayment of some Federal Financing Bank (FFB) loans financed by REA. This allowed some cooperatives who had borrowed funds at high interest rates to refinance the loans at a more attractive rate.

- Omnibus Budget Reconciliation Act of 1987
  - Authorized additional prepayments for REA-guaranteed FFB loans.

- Federal Credit Reform Act of 1990
  - Revised funding provisions for insured and guaranteed loans.
  - Eliminated the revolving fund as such.

- Rural Economic Development Act of 1990
  - Established a program for economic development, including providing loans and grants to promote rural business.
  - Provided grants for distance learning and medical link programs.

continued on page 20

FIGURE 2.3. Congress Steps In

continued from page 19

- Rural Electrification Administration Improvement Act of 1992
  - Authorized discounted prepayments of direct or insured loans.

- Omnibus Budget Reconciliation Act of 1993
  - Allowed borrowers to refinance or prepay guaranteed loans funded by the FFB with payment of a penalty.

- Rural Electrification Loan Restructuring Act of 1993 (RELRA)
  - Eliminated all 2 percent and most 5 percent loans

  - Authorized hardship loans at 5 percent

  - Established municipal rate loans with a tax exempt equivalent interest rate based on a published index of municipal rates at capped at 7 percent in some cases.

In keeping with that goal, Congress used the Rural Economic Development Act of 1990 to amend the REAct to establish a program for economic development, including providing loans and grants to promote rural business. The loans are targeted toward business start-ups or expansion projects which create jobs. Loans have been approved for such diverse projects as a hospital addition in Wisconsin, a building shell in an industrial park in Missouri, and expansion of a timber business in Louisiana.

The law also provided grants for distance learning and medical link programs to improve the uses of telecommunications and advanced computer technology to provide educational and medical benefits to rural residents.

RELRA Restructures REA Lending Programs

The Rural Electrification Loan Restructuring Act of 1993 (RELRA), enacted by Congress on November 1, 1993, brought a new round of changes to REA. The interest rate on REA loans had been a source of controversy for many years. The obvious gap between the rate at which the government borrowed money and the rate at which it was lending it for rural electric purposes—five percent for most direct loans, two percent for hardship cases—became a major issue in light of the massive federal deficit, despite other forms of subsidies to other types of utilities. Analysis by the National Rural Electric Cooperative Association indicated that at $39 per consumer the government's subsidization of electric cooperatives was far less than the subsidies afforded investor-owned utilities ($60 per consumer) and municipal utilities ($92 per consumer) through tax benefits. Nevertheless, during the 1980s, REA was frequently lending money at less than half the government's cost—a much more direct and obvious subsidy than tax benefits.

FIGURE 2.4. Interest Rate on REA Loans vs.
U.S. Cost of Money to the Government

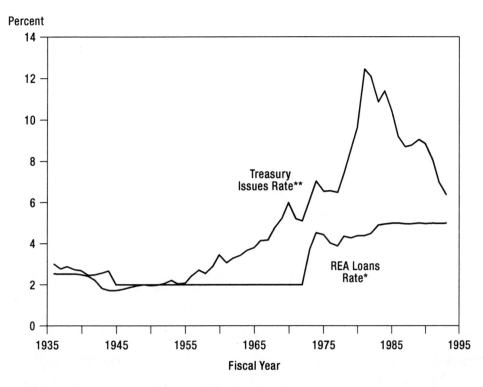

*Weighted average for loans approved during the year.
****SOURCE:** *Monthly Statement of the Public Debt of the United States, Department of the Treasury.*

In the early years of the Rural Electric Program, the interest rate on REA loans exceeded the government's cost of money. Recent changes in interest rates should narrow the gap that has existed in recent years.

SOURCE: *Report of the Adminstrator Fiscal Year 1993, U.S. Department of Agriculture, Rural Electrification Administration, 1994.*

RELRA resolved the issue by restructuring the REA direct loan programs for electric borrowers to provide municipal rate loans with an interest rate tied to a published index of municipal rates capped at seven percent in some cases and hardship loans with an interest rate of five percent for the neediest borrowers. REA continued to provide loan guarantees at an interest rate negotiated between the borrower and the lender. RELRA also changed the interest rate on telephone insured loans to a government cost-of-money rate and increased the interest rate on telephone hardship loans to five percent.

Rural Utilities Service

After almost 60 years, REA was abolished by a massive reorganization of the Department of Agriculture in 1994. Its responsibilities were transferred to a new agency, **Rural Utilities Service (RUS)**. RUS has the same mandate to improve the quality of life in rural America through loan and grant programs and to support economic development in rural areas. The electric program continues to operate much as it did under REA.

FIGURE 2.5. Key RUS Functions

- Administers the electric and telecommunications loan guarantee programs previously administered by REA.

- Administers water and waste disposal programs previously administered by the Rural Development Administration.

- Supports common goals of rural economic development and revitalizing rural communities.

Like other government agencies, RUS is exploring ways to offer better service at a lower cost. It has made and is considering further a number of changes in loan policies and procedures aimed at enhancing the agency's effectiveness and the borrower's flexibility.

The rural electric system fostered first by REA and now by RUS serves more than 30 million people over 75 percent of the geographic area of the United States. Today there are approximately 920 rural electric distribution and G&T cooperatives operating in 46 states and territories. RUS administers a $33 billion loan portfolio of electric loans to support rural electric infrastructure and leverage federal investment with private capital.

The rural telecommunications program provides service to over 15 million people in 46 states. RUS administers a $6 billion loan portfolio which supports rural telecommunications infrastructure. One of the purposes of the telecommunications program is to ensure that rural citizens have access to the same telecommunications services as their urban counterparts, including services such as the "Information Superhighway."

To that end, RUS continues to administer the Distance Learning and Medical Link Program initiated by REA in 1993. As of June 1995, the program had provided 61 grants totaling $20 million to rural schools, hospitals and medical clinics in 35 states. The purpose of the program is to encourage telecommunications services to link rural areas with educational and health services offered in urban areas.

National Cooperative Services Corporation

The National Cooperative Services Corporation (NCSC) was incorporated in February 1981 as a taxable cooperative to assist electric cooperatives in participating in unique financing opportunities which were available at that time. NCSC has arranged lease transactions and other types of specialized financing programs for G&T systems. NCSC operates under a management service agreement with CFC which allows NCSC to utilize CFC's staff as needed.

Rural Telephone Financing Cooperative

In 1987, the Rural Telephone Financing Cooperative (RTFC), an affiliate of CFC, was organized to serve the specialized financing needs of the rural telecommunications industry. Membership in RTFC is open to organizations eligible to receive funding from RUS or affiliates of such organizations. RTFC offers programs to complement traditional lending programs and offers financing for projects not authorized by the Rural Electrification Act. The organization provides financing for a wide range of financing and refinancing needs.

National Rural Telecommunications Cooperative

The National Rural Telecommunications Cooperative (NRTC) was organized by NRECA and CFC in August 1986 to provide modern television programming and telecommunications services in rural areas. By 1994, it had 800 telephone and electric members in 48 states. It provides satellite and other advanced telecommunications and media services to its members and their affiliates and is an authorized distributor of DIRECTV, a direct broadcast satellite television service.

Western Fuels

In 1974, Western Fuels Association Inc. was incorporated as a not-for-profit fuel supply cooperative serving both cooperative and municipal utilities. Western Fuels purchases and, through affiliates, mines coal for its member systems. In addition, it owns and operates two rail lines and more than 1,000 rail cars.

CHAPTER 3

COOPERATIVE SERVICE OBLIGATIONS

One of the basic principles guiding the development of the rural electric programs was that of **area coverage.** A cooperative achieved area coverage when (1) all consumers in its service areas either were served or had service available without extra charges for the construction of facilities and (2) there were no unserved communities or areas outside the co-op's present service area that it might be expected to serve. The concept extended to the issue of rates as well. Any customer located in an area served by a cooperative should receive electric service at a postage stamp rate, or the same rate as any other similar consumer in the cooperative's service area. In other words, the same rate schedules and minimum charges should apply no matter how far from or close to the cooperative's central facilities and power supply sources the consumer might be located. The principle of area coverage also applied to the extension of service into new areas. As long as the system as a whole remained workable, service would be extended into adjacent or other areas a cooperative might reasonably serve. Some cooperatives did apply special charges to consumers requiring special services, such as large commercial consumers, seasonal users and those requiring temporary service.

The Pace Act of 1944 made area coverage more economically feasible by extending the maximum loan repayment period from 25 to 35 years, thus reducing cash flow requirements and providing for a larger payback period and fixing the interest rate on REA loans at two percent. REA also supported the concept by adding an area coverage agreement to its loan documents in 1950 that required co-ops to work toward and achieve area coverage.

More than 99 percent of rural residents now have access to electricity. The area coverage goal has been largely achieved. It is interesting to note that as the electric industry becomes more competitive, utilities, including cooperatives, are considering departures from the postage stamp rates in the form of special rates and incentives for some customers in order to keep them on the system. These special pricing incentives will be discussed in later chapters.

TERRITORIAL PROTECTION

As the rural electric program brought power to areas that previously had none, some of those areas developed into attractive service territories. Housing followed the lines, and many new suburban communities, sometimes called "string towns," developed as electric service became available. Neighboring investor-owned or municipal utilities often became interested in serving those areas after the loads developed, or in serving an attractive commercial or industrial customer drawn to the new community. For cooperatives, **territorial protection**—maintaining service to these newly attractive territories—is an important issue.

For most of the past century, regulation of investor-owned utilities has been based on a regulatory compact that provides the utility with an exclusive retail service territory and allows it to recover expenses plus a reasonable return on its investment, as long as it meets the public need for service. Initially, most states did not regulate rates or other aspects of co-op operations and thus cooperatives did not have the protection of exclusive retail service areas. Cooperatives were prohibited from serving in areas assigned to other utilities, but did not receive the same protection for their service areas. Conflicts often arose when investor-owned utilities tried to expand into cooperative service areas or tried to bypass a cooperative to serve attractive commercial and industrial loads in cooperative service areas.

Most states have now adopted some method of assigning territory to cooperatives. Normally, the state public service commission is responsible for resolving territorial disputes. In some states, co-ops have accepted rate or other regulation in return for such territorial guarantees.

As arms of local governments, however, municipal systems are usually exempt from statewide territorial agreements, and service area disputes frequently arise as cities grow. In many areas, a utility's franchise (or service area) and the municipal city limits are identical. When a municipality annexes adjacent territory being served by a cooperative, in most states the service territory passes to the investor-owned or municipal utility serving within the borders of the municipality. The cooperative may not be compensated for the full value of its facilities in the area, and the resulting loss of consumers means a loss of revenue and thus higher costs for remaining members. At some point, the cogeneration will no longer be able to function as a viable organization. In addition, if the cooperative is a member of a G&T, the G&T will experience a loss of expected load growth and revenues from power not sold.

This is a very serious problem for some electric co-ops. Negotiations have settled some disputes through territorial swaps or compensation payments from the utility taking over service. However, in some states co-ops have turned to the legislature for protection—a step that is usually strongly opposed by municipal utilities. At the national level, too, NRECA has worked with congressional supporters to protect its members from the loss of prime service territory, but so far without success.

QUALITY OF SERVICE

All utilities, including electric cooperatives, have a fundamental obligation and duty to provide safe and reliable service to all consumers within their service territories and to expand their facilities to meet growth and new consumer requirements. There are, however, practical limitations to this obligation. A cooperative is not required to serve where conditions, such as terrain, are beyond its control. Nor is a cooperative required to serve a member that fails to observe cooperative rules, tampers with meters or other equipment, uses defective equipment, or fails to pay bills on time. While RUS loan documents continue to support the concept of area coverage, a cooperative is not expected to provide service outside of its existing service area limits if it is not economically feasible.

A cooperative is also obligated to provide adequate service. Adequate service is that level of service that is free from unnecessary or avoidable interruptions. Adequate service is safe and does not endanger members or their property. There should be no undue discrimination or differences in the quality of service provided to an individual member or class of members. An important part of providing adequate service is developing routine maintenance programs and providing timely system upgrades in order to avoid deteriorations in the quality of service.

Regulatory Control over Service Quality

State public service commissions generally have regulatory authority over the quality of service provided by investor-owned utilities. In states where the rates of electric cooperatives are regulated by the commission, quality of service is usually also subject to regulations. In states where the commission does not regulate the rates of cooperatives, the commission may regulate the quality of service, particularly if there is some other form of regulation, such as territorial assignment. In North Carolina, for example, the North Carolina Utilities Commission does not regulate the rates of cooperative or municipal utilities. It does assign service territories to cooperatives, while areas served by municipal utilities remain unassigned territory. The Commission has exercised regulatory authority over service issues through its ability to assign cooperative or municipal territory to another utility. Some states do not regulate cooperative quality of service at all.

RUS monitors the quality of service in several ways. First, cooperatives are required to meet the specifications and service standards established by RUS. This ensures that the systems use quality materials and good construction practices. RUS has adopted the standards established by the National Electric Safety Code, which is the normal industry standard. The code addresses the safety aspects of design, construction, operations, and maintenance for electric supply, telephone, CATV, and railroad signal utilities, both public and private. The standards are also applicable to industrial companies that generate electricity for their own use. In the case of electric power, the code applies to generation, transmission, and distribution up to the point of delivery to the customer. REA requires a cooperative's engineer to certify that new facilities are designed to meet code requirements as a condition of loan approval. In addition, RUS monitors outage rates, or the average hours of outage per consumer per year, and requires an operations and maintenance survey—which includes a visual inspection of facilities—every three years. If the condition of the system or the quality and reliability of the service is unacceptable, these issues can be addressed in the loan approval process.

State commissions have considered it part of their statutory duty to develop and determine service standards. Investigations to determine adequate service requirements have been conducted directly by them or in cooperation with technical and professional associations, educational institutions, utility associations, individual utilities, and the National Institute of Standards and Technology. The National Association of Regulatory Utility Commissioners also has a committee on service of public utilities.

Service Standards
The development of service standards is a continuing process. As technologies and procedures change and improve, cooperatives and other utilities take an active part in revising and updating operating standards. This attention to service standards by all interested parties indicates recognition of the importance of this issue. Whether or not a cooperative is regulated by the public service commission in its state, the standards set by the commission, RUS, and other regulatory agencies are generally considered to be minimum requirements. The actual service offered is expected to be on a higher level of performance.

Electric cooperatives, in their efforts to provide safe, adequate and reliable service, face many of the same challenges confronting other types of utilities. They also face challenges which are unique to the co-ops, including distance and terrain. Operating conditions may affect the adequacy and efficiency of generating facilities, transmission and distribution facilities, and metering equipment. From the consumer's viewpoint, continuity of service and of voltage stability are the most important aspects of satisfactory electric service. Most systems have standby facilities, duplicate or alternate lines, and interconnection with other sources of supply to prevent interruptions in service. Temporary interruptions do occur, however, as a result of weather conditions, fires, and other conditions. Overall, electric cooperatives have a strong record of providing reliable service and prompt restoration of service after interruptions.

Even momentary outages caused by events such as tree limbs or squirrels touching power lines can be a problem for consumers using sophisticated electronic equipment, such as computers. Good right-of-way maintenance and installation of equipment to shield vulnerable facilities from animals can reduce the problem. New technology offers insulated cable which is not subject to this type of interruption. Today, the consumer is much more sensitive to outages which may have gone completely unnoticed in the past. However brief the interruption, a consumer may be more annoyed by a computer shut-down than by a more serious problem which does not have a noticeable effect.

Sometimes the problem is not with the quality of service delivered by the cooperative but with the wiring in the home or office. A state-of-the-art computer may be plugged into an outlet that was wired more than 40 years ago and may not even be grounded. In such cases the cooperative can work with the member to find ways to improve the situation.

A copy of the terms and conditions for electric service, including relevant service standards, is usually given to each member joining the cooperative and may also be on file with the state regulatory commission. The following things may be included.

General. The procedures for joining the cooperative, the rules governing receipt of electric service, and the relationship between the cooperative and its members.

Operation and Maintenance. Issues such as maintaining adequate service, and reporting requirements related to service, and possibly wiring specifications as well as provisions for identifying and inspecting poles.

Meters. Specifications concerning acceptable locations for meters, meter-testing facilities, equipment, and standards. Accuracy requirements of watt-hour, demand, and time meters. Places, methods, and times for testing meters. Procedures for determining adjustment of bills in the event of meter malfunction.

Member Information. Information concerning reading of meters, bills and billing, lighting, and other services as well as the filing of rate schedules, rules, and regulations is also included.

Voltage and Frequency. Standard nominal voltage and permissible variations with respect to both lighting service and power service, standard frequency and voltage surveys and records are noted.

Charges, Deposits, and Refunds. Provisions for meter rentals, billing adjustments, and customer deposits, including when deposits may be required, when they are to be returned, and payment of interest on deposit.

Accidents. Reporting and prevention of accidents.

Line Extension Policy. Procedures for extending lines to serve new customers and facilities.

SERVICE EXTENSIONS

From time to time, a cooperative needs to acquire additional land for new facilities to meet the members' growing needs. The cooperative can acquire title to the land outright, or it can obtain an **easement**, the right to use the land for a limited purpose while another person retains the other rights of ownership. Initially, cooperatives were able to obtain easements and rights-of-way at no cost: it was part of the cooperative philosophy that members would contribute land for the common good. Cooperatives are sometimes able to do that today, but with the rise in real estate values and suburbanization of many co-op service territories, it is no longer practical in some areas. If a co-op member is unwilling to donate land, the co-op can usually negotiate a reasonable purchase of the necessary rights.

In cases where a private owner refuses to negotiate, the cooperative may be able to exercise the power of **eminent domain**. Eminent domain allows land to be taken from a private owner for a greater public good. Depending on the law and regulatory structure in its state, a co-op may be able to condemn the property it needs.

Public use. Several provisions of both federal and state constitutions have been interpreted to require that the land be taken only if the proposed project benefits the public use or welfare. Since cooperative facilities are used to benefit the public, this requirement has not posed a significant problem.

Necessity. The taking must be necessary. Courts will generally defer to the commission or the cooperative decision and will not upset the order without a showing of gross abuses.

Compensation. Most eminent domain disputes concern the amount to be paid to the person whose land is taken. Constitutional provisions require the payment of "just" compensation, which has usually been interpreted by the courts to mean a fair market price. Courts still have to determine what interests are compensable (for example, should an adjoining landowner recover if a cooperative takes land that impairs access to his property?), when the property should be valued, and how the market price should be determined.

While it is useful to have legal procedures that enable a cooperative to obtain land for the facilities needed to provide power to its members, negotiations leading to a satisfactory arrangement with the landowner—who is likely to be a member of the cooperative as well—lead to better member relations. The cooperative concept is that of a group working together for the benefit of all members. A member who refuses to reach a reasonable settlement when his land is needed is not living up to his responsibility. Neither is a cooperative management that fails to respect and meet the needs and concerns of an individual member.

RELIABLE SERVICE THROUGH POWER POOLS

Cooperatives participate in a variety of regional organizations that provide arrangements for interconnections and intersystem transactions for handling bulk power supplies safely, economically, and reliably. The prevention and quick termination of occasional blackouts, or widespread outages due to system failures, and lesser service interruptions are generally managed by such groups.

On November 9, 1965 a major power failure struck the Northeastern United States and Ontario, Canada. In response, the industry formed the North American Electric Reliability Council (NERC), formerly known as the National Electric Reliability Council, in 1968 to promote the reliability of the electricity supply for North America. NERC helps electricity suppliers work together to ensure adequate power supply in North America by reviewing the past for lessons learned, monitoring the present for compliance with policies, criteria, standards, and guides, and assessing the future reliability of the bulk systems.

NERC is a not-for-profit corporation owned by nine Regional Councils. The membership of the Regional Councils includes systems from all ownership segments of the electric industry, including investor-owned, federal, cooperative, state, municipal, and provincial utilities, independent power producers, power marketers, and electricity brokers. This group accounts for virtually all the electricity supplied in the United States, Canada, and the northern portion of Baja California, Mexico. The transmission systems of the members of the regional councils are interconnected, creating flexible regional systems that allow the transfer of power to areas facing an emergency.

In addition to these councils, there are a number of regional power pools established by individual systems. To qualify for membership in a typical pool, a cooperative or other public utility must (1) be engaged in the generation and sale of electricity directly or indirectly for the use of the general public, (2) be directly interconnected with one or more of the other pool members, and (3) agree to follow the basic rules of pool operation. Some cooperatives choose to be represented by others in the pool because of the significant expense—including the requirement of dedicating significant staff time to the pool—associated with pool membership.

Recently the Federal Energy Regulatory Commission (FERC) has adopted policies and procedures encouraging the formation of **regional transmission groups (RTGs)**. An RTG is defined by FERC as "a voluntary organization of transmission owners, transmission users, and other entities interested in coordinating transmission planning (and expansion), operation and use on a regional (and interregional) basis." The RTGs would make it easier to provide transmission services to potential users and to find voluntary ways to resolve disputes over transmission services. FERC has said that it will give great weight to decisions made by RTGs if the RTG mitigates the market power of transmission owners and provides for fair decision-making.

CHAPTER 4

MEMBER RELATIONS

Member support is the key to any cooperative's success. In the early days of rural electrification, this was no problem. The arrival of electricity had been eagerly anticipated, and every rural family had a story about what they did the day the lights went on. Members were grateful for the ways in which electricity made their lives easier and more productive. Many actively participated in the organization and operation of the cooperative. Initially, the size of the cooperative was small enough that the members knew each other, the board members, and management.

While this attitude still exists in some areas, more and more members today view the cooperative as any other power company. They are interested in good service and low costs compared to neighboring power suppliers.

Cooperatives still have some very potent tools to use in fostering and maintaining strong positive member relations. The most important of these is the ability to provide high quality service.

Successful member service programs have several things in common. One is that the board of directors and senior management must lead, not just point the way. A genuine commitment of time and effort reinforces the cooperative philosophy and can bring changes when needed. The board and management must set the tone, the pace, and the example.

An important aspect of maintaining quality of service is maintaining a strong commitment to member service ethic among the co-op's employees. Carroll Electric Membership Corporation in Carrollton, Georgia, is one system that is achieving this. The manager holds group meetings with employees each year to emphasize that the consumer-member—not the manager, not the board of directors, not other employees—is the reason they are there. He emphasizes that when the member asks for something, the co-op should find a way to do it.

An example of that was the elimination of the co-op's fuel adjustment charge. Carroll's members complained that they didn't understand the charge and that it was difficult to budget for power bills. In response, the co-op developed a method for projecting the year's fuel costs and includes it in its base rate. If the cooperative overcollects fuel costs, it applies a credit in the next year. If it undercollects, there is a surcharge. Either way, the member knows what the cost of electricity will be.

Carroll has found other innovative ways to provide good service to its members and build member loyalty. The cooperative worked with a local bank to develop a special credit card program. Members who have a good paying record with the co-op are pre-approved for a credit card with the bank. They can also use the card to pay their electric bill.

The cooperative offers a home security service which is tied to a remote meter reading service. The remote meter reading system also allows the member to specify the meter reading date.

Carroll's newest program involves the geothermal heating and cooling market. The co-op will install and maintain the outside loop required for such systems at a monthly cost of $5.50 per ton of air conditioning capacity. The offer applies to both new and retrofitted systems. The more efficient system is expected to save consumers $11 per month, so the cooperative is essentially splitting the savings with the member. The program, which is starting a one-year test, not only gives the consumer-member a more economical, and efficient source of heating and cooling but also establishes a long-term relationship between the cooperative and the member. It gives the member a stake in the cooperative that will be increasingly important as competition for customers increases.

Giving Employees the Tools to Provide Good Member Service

One of the service-oriented terms in vogue today is "empowerment." That means providing employees with the resources needed to achieve their goals, whether those resources are materials, money, space, time, technology, or additional personnel to enable them to provide better service to the membership. Are the linemen equipped with the things they need to do the job well? Does the office have a private place where a member may discuss a sensitive problem? Do employees have sufficient time to properly complete a task, or are schedules severely overbooked? Do employees receive the training needed to enable them to do a better job? These types of considerations constitute employee empowerment for better member service.

Good member service rests on the skills and knowledge an individual brings to the job and a supportive environment. In addition to training employees to improve specific job skills, the co-op leadership must look at the environment in which those employees will function. That environment includes the information provided to the employee, the tools and materials available, and the incentives for performance.

Communicating with Members

One of the most important components of quality service is communication with the members. Listening for and understanding the needs of members and communicating clear and accurate information about the cooperative are often difficult and challenging tasks.

TEN CUSTOMER SERVICE COMMANDMENTS

When Associated Electric Cooperative (a G&T serving 43 cooperatives in Missouri and Iowa) created its "Marketing 2000" program, quality and customer service were fundamental factors. As reported in the July 1, 1991 issue of *Public Utilities Fortnightly,* the group came up with ten rules of consumer service that make the difference in marketing success. Briefly, they are as follows:

1. *Flexibility.* Make sure that policies and procedures are meeting customer needs. Make changes in operations to ensure that these needs are being met.

2. *Accessibility.* Ensure that customers have easy access to the company. Make sure you have adequate office hours and phone lines.

3. *Responsiveness.* Handle requests promptly and efficiently. Maintain courtesy and cooperation and foster an eagerness to solve problems.

4. *Expertise.* Provide consumers with informed, knowledgeable details on technical subjects. This requires well-trained professional personnel.

5. *Teamwork.* Make sure that all personnel know that consumer relations are very important. Avoid the "that's not my department" mentality.

6. *Versatility.* Respond to requests with a wide variety of options.

7. *Market Knowledge.* Conduct research and seek input and suggestions from consumers to make sure you know their expectations and attitudes.

8. *Custom-tailored Service.* Determine what customers need and fill that need.

9. *Complaint Handling.* Make sure you get complaints. Most consumers don't complain; they just stop buying a product. When you get a complaint, fast action is essential. Begin with an apology; correct the problem; and follow up.

10. *Follow-up.* This is the function that reinforces everything you do. A phone call, visit or letter provides valuable input and shows that you care about quality.

The cooperative's employees all have a role to play in enhancing the co-op's relationship with its members. Those who process bills, orders, and complaints, read meters, install service, or work as telephone operators all have many opportunities to create a good image—or a bad one. The men and women involved in repair and construction and other activities in the field create public impressions both through the way they work and how they relate to people in the community.

Employees can have a significant influence on the public's overall image of the cooperative. The public tends to believe what an employee says about his or her company. Cooperative management must provide information to employees in clear, easily understood terms in order for the employee to play their part in informing members.

All strong cooperatives rely to one degree or another on member feedback, including surveys, personal visits, member advisory committees, and follow-ups. Many tools are available for keeping the member informed, including speaker bureaus, newsletters, and youth programs. The statewide associations offer a wide range of support, including magazines, leadership development programs, information campaigns, and safety programs. Each cooperative can choose from these many options to tailor a program to meet its specific needs.

COOPERATIVE CONTRIBUTIONS

The rural electric program has made a valuable contribution to the nation. The loan and guarantee programs along with the technical support provided by REA and now RUS have brought electricity to millions of people, some of whom otherwise would probably not have access to reliable, economic sources of power even today. The availability of electricity has enabled people living and working in rural areas to be more productive and to enjoy the same standard of living as their urban counterparts.

In supporting the cooperative concept, REA empowered rural consumers by giving them a way to obtain an important resource through their own efforts, to participate in its management, and to share the benefits of that resource. By pioneering the concepts of area coverage and postage stamp rates, the co-ops made a valuable contribution to the electric industry. Cooperative leaders used the experience they gained in creating the distribution systems to develop a network of cooperative organizations, including G&Ts, statewides, and national cooperatives, to support their members' interests and needs.

Electric cooperatives are important businesses in their communities, supporting activities from economic development to health care in order to meet local needs. And rural electric cooperatives aren't just rural anymore. With electricity, many formerly rural areas have developed into thriving suburban centers of modern life.

PART

2

GENERATION AND DISTRIBUTION OF POWER

CHAPTER 5

PROVIDING ELECTRICITY TO COOPERATIVE CONSUMERS

Most members of electric cooperatives don't really care what electricity is; they value the services it provides. It gives them light, refrigeration, hot water, and color TV. It powers irrigation pumps and grain dryers. It runs the computers needed by small businesses. Electricity does these things so well that consumers don't even think about it until it isn't there. To most people, electricity is a service— a vital one that provides the necessities and amenities of modern life.

As the electric utility industry becomes more competitive and issues such as retail wheeling and marketing of electricity as a brand name commodity become critical to the survival of utilities, it is helpful to have a good understanding of the physical characteristics of electricity and knowledge of its generation and transmission. In the next few pages we will briefly review what electricity is and how it is produced and delivered to customers.

In order to understand electricity in a more physical sense, it is necessary to know something about the nature of matter. All matter is composed of atoms, which, in turn, are composed of subatomic particles. The nucleus, or the central part of the atom, contains positively charged protons and neutral neutrons. Negatively charged electrons revolve around the nucleus, much the way the earth revolves around the sun. Certain conditions can cause the electrons to flow from one atom to another. This flow of electrons is called **electricity**.

Conductors are materials in which electrons flow easily. Electricity is generated when an electric conductor moves through a magnetic field. Electricity can also be created by a chemical reaction, such as the one that occurs in a battery or fuel cell. With today's technology, the method capable of providing large amounts of electricity is that of the movement of a conductor through a magnetic field. Other approaches for generating electricity, such as photovoltaics and fuel cells, are under study, but they are not yet practical on a large scale.

Electricity has been the subject of scientific curiosity and study for centuries. Its potential for practical application, however, was not realized until the mid-1800s. Inventions such as the electric motor, direct current generator, arc light, and incandescent light were among the most important. Thomas Edison combined these developments into a practical system for the commercial generation and distribution of electricity at the Pearl Street Station, which started operation in

New York on September 4, 1882. Edison and his staff devised the entire system for distributing the electricity including underground conduit, switches, fuses, light sockets, and metering. Although it was comparatively small, serving a maximum of 106 electric lamps, the Pearl Street system contained essentially all the major functions of a modern electric company.

HOW ELECTRICITY IS GENERATED

Today, the electric generators used by G&T cooperatives still convert mechanical energy, or motion, into electric energy just as Edison's did. In these generators, a large magnet is rotated inside huge coils of wire to produce electricity. In a conventional electric power plant, the magnet is rotated at a high speed by a turbine. The turbine, made up of rows of blades on a shaft, is made to spin when a fluid or gas is forced against the blades.

In a conventional fossil-fueled steam plant, pressurized steam provides that force. The steam is produced by burning a fuel, such as coal or natural gas, in a boiler. In a nuclear plant, the heat given off by fissioning, or splitting atoms in a nuclear reactor, changes the water to steam.

FIGURE 5.1. Generation of Electricity

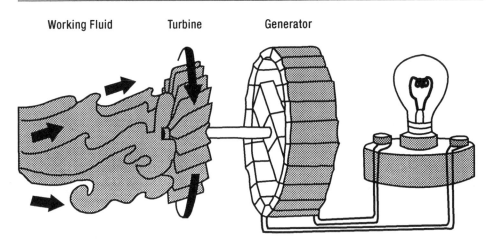

Working Fluid Turbine Generator

Electricity is produced when a magnet is rotated inside coils of wire.

As the steam passes through the turbine, it gives up most of its energy to make the blades spin. When the steam leaves the turbine, it is condensed back to water and is pumped back to the boiler, where the cycle starts over again. Condensing the steam requires a large amount of cooling water, which is why almost all large power plants are located near oceans, rivers or lakes. Where water is not available, cooling towers condense the steam back to water.

Another type of generating plant, the gas turbine, is widely used to provide **peaking capacity**. That is, the equipment is used to meet daily or seasonal demand peaks—short periods when consumers use much more power. Essentially a jet engine, the gas turbine burns a pressurized mixture of fuel and air to spin a turbine.

The **combined-cycle plant**, a relatively new design, uses the waste heat from a gas turbine to run a second steam turbine similar to that of a conventional power plant. Reusing the heat makes combined-cycle power plants more efficient than conventional power plants. A typical U.S. conventional steam unit operates at about 35 percent efficiency, while a typical combined-cycle plant has an efficiency of more than 40 percent. Combined-cycle technology is continuing to improve. A plant built by General Electric Company which began operation in South Korea in 1993 operates at 50 percent efficiency. The gas-fired combined-cycle plants also emit virtually no sulfur dioxide or fine airborne ash, and much lower levels of carbon dioxide, nitrous oxides, and other pollutants than coal-fired plants.

In addition to the generating equipment, fossil power plants will have some or all of the following facilities, depending on the type of fuel burned: fuel unloading and handling, fuel processing, fuel storage, equipment to control emissions of pollutants, and waste disposal.

In hydroelectric plants, the energy to turn the generator comes from the force of falling water. The source of the water is usually a lake or reservoir located high above the turbines, although some smaller plants have been designed to operate with height differences of 20 feet or less.

Most of the nation's best hydroelectric generating sites have already been tapped, largely by the Army Corps of Engineers and the Interior Department's Bureau of Reclamation. A series of massive dams on the country's largest rivers—such as the Tennessee, the Missouri, the Columbia and their tributaries—provide thousands of megawatts of capacity. New hydroelectric capacity will be limited to smaller operations, and this type of generation is not expected to grow significantly as a percentage of the nation's overall supply.

Another type of peaking plant—pumped storage—is being used on a pilot basis at two G&Ts. Oglethorpe Power Corporation in Georgia uses conventionally produced power to pump water to fill an artificial mountaintop lake during the night, when other demands are lowest. As demand climbs during the day, the water is released to flow through huge pipes to a turbine on an 800-megawatt generator.

Alabama Electric Cooperative also makes use of the overnight demand drop to fill an underground chamber with compressed air. By releasing the air through a turbine, the G&T can produce up to 110 megawatts of additional power to meet peak demands.

Both plants store potential energy, not electricity. Oglethorpe uses falling water and Alabama Electric uses escaping pressurized air to spin turbines, which in turn generate electricity for consumer use. Although both systems must use electricity

FIGURE 5.2. Cooperative Generating Capacity, 1993

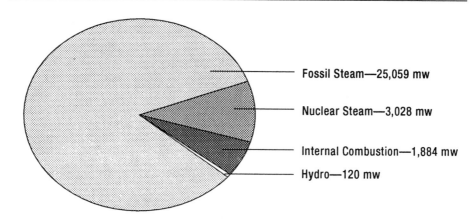

SOURCE: *Rural Electrification Administration*

**Although graph indicates co-ops only have 120 mw of hydro capacity, they rely heavily on federal power agencies that have a lot of hydro capacity.

U.S. Generating Capacity, 1993

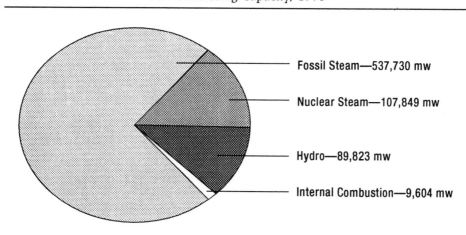

SOURCE: *Statistical Yearbook of the Electric Utility Industry, Edison Electric Institute, 1993 Edition*

to store this potential energy, the benefits of having additional capacity available at peak periods of demand make it an economic facility.

Key Definitions

To better understand the flow of electricity through a conductor we will use the analogy of water flowing through a pipe. In the water pipe, the pressure of the water is expressed in pounds per square inch. Similarly, the "pressure" of the electricity in a conductor is expressed by the term **volts**. The quantity of water flowing through a pipe is expressed in gallons per minute; for electricity, the quantity flowing through a conductor is expressed in **amperes** or amps. There is no clear analogy to the water pipe for the term **watt**. The watt is a measure of the capacity to do work and is equal to the product of the voltage times the amperage.

Electrical capacity is measured in **kilowatts** (KW) or **megawatts** (MW). Each KW is equivalent to 1,000 watts; each MW is equivalent to a million watts.

FIGURE 5.3.

volts x amps = watts

1,000 watts x 1 hour = 1 Kwh

100 watts x 10 hours = 1 Kwh

10 watts x 100 hours = 1 Kwh

Returning to the water analogy, the total amount of water used can be measured in gallons. The amount of electricity used is measured in **kilowatt-hours** (Kwh). This may also be reported in megawatt-hours (MWH), or 1,000 Kwh. A kilowatt-hour is equivalent to 1,000 watts of electrical energy used for one hour. For example, ten 100-watt light bulbs burning for one hour would use one kilowatt-hour of electricity, as would one 100-watt light bulb burning for 10 hours or one 10-watt bulb burning for 100 hours.

Once generated, electricity must be delivered directly to the consumers for immediate use since it cannot readily be stored. Although batteries can store electricity (and were actually used commercially for that purpose around the turn of the century), their application in today's electric power systems is extremely limited. Research is under way, however, into new high-capacity batteries which may become part of electric distribution systems in the future.

Transmission and Distribution of Electric Power

The system needed to transport electricity from the generating plant where it is created to the point at which it is delivered to the consumer is similar in concept to the transportation network surrounding a large city. For example, major highways are used to move large amounts of traffic out of the downtown area. Interchanges on the highway let vehicles leave for the local network of streets to reach their final destinations. Electricity leaves the power plant by electrical highways known as high-voltage transmission lines. These are heavy wires held aloft by large steel towers 50 to 100 feet high. These transmission lines operate at voltages from 138,000 volts to as high as 750,000 volts.

When power plants are located in urban and suburban areas where there is no room for overhead transmission lines, underground high-voltage transmission cables are used. This usually entails using a special oil-filled coaxial cable or extensive ductwork to provide cooling for the cable. In contrast, primary lines for residential service can usually be buried directly in the ground. In addition, transmission cables must be buried much deeper than distribution cables and may require special shielding because of safety considerations. As a result, underground transmission is substantially more expensive than overhead lines.

FIGURE 5.4. Generation, Transmission and Distribution of Electricity

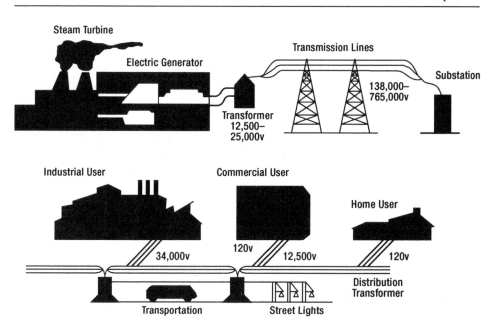

Typically, a G&T Cooperative generates and transmits electricity to member distribution systems that deliver it to consumer-members.

High-voltage transmission lines are used to interconnect power plants and to transmit large quantities of electricity to areas where it is needed. The vast majority of customers, however, cannot use the electricity at the high voltage of the transmission line. Nor is it any more practical to build these lines close to every customer than it would be to build an interstate highway to every neighborhood.

At intervals, therefore, some of the electricity is tapped off the transmission line at a facility known as a substation. There the voltage of the electricity is reduced by a transformer to a much lower level, usually 12,000 volts. The lower voltage permits much smaller power lines to be built and permits more economical underground transmission of electricity if needed. Although some industrial and commercial customers can use electricity supplied at "pressures" of 12,000 volts or higher, the majority of customers require a lower voltage. Homes use 120/240 volts. A transformer is usually located within several hundred feet of the customer to step down, or reduce, the voltage.

Because electric cooperatives serve predominantly in rural areas, their density—about 6 consumers per mile of distribution line—is low relative to that of other types of utilities. Investor-owned utilities, for example, serve an average of 35 consumers per mile of line, while municipal utilities serve an average of 48 consumers per mile of line.

The kilowatt-hours of electricity used by a customer are measured by a watt-hour meter or, better known simply as an electric meter. The electric meter is an electric motor connected to a series of pointers or dials on the meter face. As electricity is used by the customer, it flows through the motor, causing it to turn and move the pointers. The more electricity used, the faster the meter's motor turns. The faces of the dials are calibrated in Kwh. Some newer meters use digital displays instead of dials. The amount of electricity a consumer uses during a period is determined by comparing the meter readings at the beginning and end of the period.

How Generating Units Are Dispatched

In order to operate efficiently and provide reliable power at the lowest cost, the supply of electricity must be tailored to the ups and downs of consumer demands. When all the consuming sectors—homes, farms, businesses, and industry—are using electricity at once, the cooperative must be ready to meet that demand. It must also be ready to cut back when demand falls. Because of the varied schedules on which consumers use electricity, the load varies over the course of the day, the week, and the year, and also depends on weather and economic conditions.

A cooperative's minimum load is called its **base load**, which is often defined as the amount of capacity which must be available to meet the minimum requirements on a weekday during the peak week. Essentially, the base load must be met year round. Base load generating capacity requires a high degree of availability. Because it is operated continuously, except for scheduled maintenance outages, it should have a low variable or operating cost. Historically, power suppliers have

FIGURE 5.5. Typical Annual Load Duration Curve

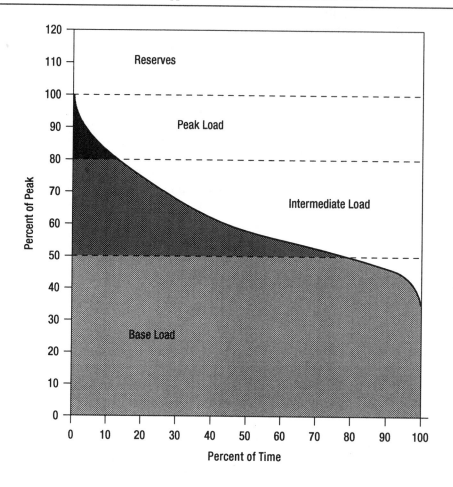

been willing to pay higher capital costs for base load capacity, because the investment can be recovered through sales of billions of kilowatt-hours.

On the other hand, the **peak demand**—the maximum demand ever placed on an electric system—usually must be met only for a short time. Most peaking units are designed to operate less than 2,000 hours per year. Historically, since the units are operated in such short bursts, power suppliers have been willing to pay higher operating costs in return for lower capital investments.

Intermediate loads are those which fall between base and peak loads. Intermediate capacity is sometimes supplied by older, less efficient units which may have originally been base load units. Ideally, however, an intermediate—or cycling—unit should be capable of rapid changes in level of output to meet changes in load. Some of the generating units under construction today are designed to meet intermediate loads.

This traditional planning model has been affected by recent advances in gas turbine technology. Now combustion turbines that used to be limited to peaking use are capable of base load or intermediate service in highly efficient combined cycle applications.

Power suppliers must also have reserves, or extra capacity available to meet needs during outages. The appropriate level of reserves depends on such factors as the size and number of generating units and the capacity available through interconnections with other utilities.

Distribution cooperatives usually have little input into the way power supply sources are dispatched. A G&T cooperative or other power supplier, however, typically must choose among many different generating plants to meet different types of loads. The decision about which generators will be operated at any given time is made by a dispatcher. In assigning load to each generator, the dispatcher considers:

- The cost of electricity from the generator

- The generator's maximum capacity

- Each generator's maintenance requirements

- How much spare generating capacity must be maintained to ensure reliable system operations

- Environmental considerations

- Whether lower cost power is available from other sources, such as other utilities or independent power producers

Failure to match electric supply to demand can result in voltage reductions, or brownouts, and even blackouts, or actual loss of service in a large area. To help prevent such problems, cooperatives have joined other power suppliers to form regional power pools. Members of each pool agree to share reserve generating capacity and to assist each other in times of emergency. By coordinating the dispatch of their respective generating units, they also reduce the overall costs of power production—and maintaining reserves.

CHAPTER 6

MEETING FUTURE POWER REQUIREMENTS

Electricity consumption by U.S. cooperative consumers has grown steadily. In the post-war years of 1945–50, megawatt-hour sales to consumers grew at an average rate of more than 30 percent per year as both the number of cooperatives and number of consumers they served grew and existing consumers increased their use of electricity with new appliances and uses. Cooperatives have routinely experienced higher growth rates than other segments of the industry due to continued electrification and the suburbanization of some cooperative service territories. Annual growth was robust during the decades of the 1950s (14.4 percent per year) and 1960s (10.2 percent) as well as the early part of the 1970s (9.3 percent a year through 1976). Like other segments of the industry, cooperatives experienced an abrupt reduction in the rate of growth in the late 1970s. Growth slipped to 5.7 percent per year from 1976 to 1980, 3.0 percent a year during the 1980–85 period, and 2.2 percent through 1990. The early 1990s brought some recovery with an average annual growth in kilowatt-hour sales of 3.9 percent from 1990 to 1993. Peak demand on cooperative systems has also continued to increase.

The decline in load growth experienced during the late 1970s and 1980s was not anticipated by most cooperative systems, and many of the G&Ts continued scheduled construction programs. The G&Ts' installed generating capacity grew from less than 6,000 MW in 1970 to 17,119 MW in 1980 to 29,283 MW in 1985. Growth slowed after that, however, and G&Ts added less than 3,000 MW by the end of 1993. Many areas now have surplus generating capacity, and few new power plants are planned or under construction. G&T construction work in progress fell from a high of more than $11 billion in 1983 to about $1 billion in 1993. While the G&Ts are not expected to have large capital requirements for generation in the next few years, they will continue to invest in transmission and other facilities.

Growth in the electric industry as a whole followed a similar pattern. Between 1975 and 1980, megawatt-hour sales by the total electric utility industry grew at an average annual rate of 4.2 percent. That dropped to 1.6 percent for the 1980–1985 period and 3.2 percent for the 1985–1990 period. Growth slipped again during the early 1990s with an average annual growth rate of 1.7 percent for the 1990–93 period. In general, growth in electricity consumption follows the path of economic growth in the United States. During the 1994–2004 period, the

FIGURE 6.1. Cooperative Installed Generating Capacity (MW)

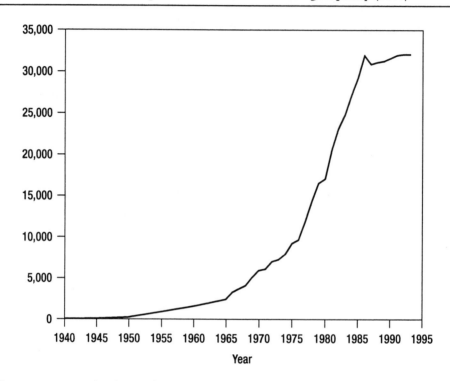

The G&T systems made substantial capacity additions in the 1970s and 1980s.
SOURCE: *Rural Utilities Service, 1995*

North American Electric Reliability Council (NERC) predicts, total electricity sales in the United States will grow at an average rate of 1.8 percent annually.

Unlike the G&Ts, other power suppliers plan to keep adding generating capacity over the next several years. NERC forecasts capacity additions totaling 73,387 MW during the 1994–2003 period. In contrast, capacity additions during the 1983–93 period totaled 128,196 MW.

As a result of this lower rate of addition, NERC estimates that U.S. summer capacity reserve margins will shrink from 20.1 percent in 1994 to 16.5 percent in 2003. With this slowing of growth, the industry has placed less emphasis on building large base load power plants. In this climate, the emergence of combined-cycle technology offers an important advantage. It can be built in stages, with the gas turbine installed first and used for peaking purposes and the steam turbine installed later when continuous loads require it. Most new capacity constructed in the next few years is likely to be intermediate and small peaking units.

New Technology and Natural Gas Dominate New Generation

Since 1970, Congress has enacted several major pieces of legislation aimed at protecting the environment, including the National Environmental Policy Act, the Clean Air Act, the Federal Water Pollution Control Act, the Federal Lands Policy and Management Act, the Resource Conservation and Recovery Act, and the Clean Air Act Amendments of 1990. These laws together with state laws and initiatives have affected the generation of electricity in many ways. For example, coal-fired plants must have special equipment to prevent the emission of potentially harmful pollutants to the air. Waste water must be treated to control its temperature and remove pollutants before it is released to a river or lake. Generators are encouraged to use the best available control technology to minimize and eliminate, if possible, the release of potential pollutants from new units.

Changes in the regulatory structure of the natural gas industry and advances in gas technology, along with these environmental concerns, have combined to make natural gas an attractive fuel for power generation. According to NERC, more than 70 percent of utility capacity planned or under construction is capable of burning oil or natural gas. Almost half of operating independent power projects burn natural gas.

Advanced gas technology offers several advantages. It has efficiencies approaching 50 percent. It can be used both for new generation and for repowering existing plants. It has a lower capital cost than a coal-fired plant as well as a shorter construction time.

Natural gas also offers major environmental benefits. Gas boilers emit virtually no SO_2 or particulate matter, and emissions of other air pollutants such as CO_2 and NO_x are significantly lower than for comparably sized coal units. Very little, if any, additional pollution control equipment is required.

Clean coal technology also offers benefits to electric generators. Circulating fluidized bed combustion units burn coal in a bed of ash, sand, and limestone. Sulfur released from the burning coal reacts with the limestone to form solid calcium compounds. The fluidized bed operates at a lower temperature than a conventional boiler, which reduces the production of NO_x. Circulating fluidized bed technology can also be used to burn waste materials, such as wood waste and municipal solid waste.

A number of manufacturers now offer gas turbines in the 1–50 MW range which can be installed quickly and moved to new sites in response to changes in load conditions. Some are aeroderivatives adapted from turbine designs used to power jet aircraft. Others have evolved from industrial products, such as those used in refineries. An emerging use of this new technology is for **dispersed generation**, that is smaller units which are strategically placed throughout a power supply system, rather than at a central location.

Cooperatives may find these units attractive for several uses in the future. First, they can be sited at substations to strengthen the grid and thus delay larger capacity additions until they are more cost effective. Second, they can be used to provide power directly to large users in a cogeneration project as part of a competitive strategy for keeping consumers from leaving the system. Finally, some cooperatives may find these small units an attractive option compared to other power supply alternatives.

JOINT PARTICIPATION PROJECTS

In 1963, Buckeye Power, Inc., an Ohio G&T, and Ohio Power Company, a subsidiary of American Electric Power Company, Inc., took the unprecedented step of building a power plant together. They agreed to share ownership of the Cardinal Station, two 615-MW coal-fired units. Other agreements between Buckeye and Ohio Power gave the co-op access to transmission and **wheeling,** in which transmission facilities of one system are used to transmit power produced by another. Buckeye obtained its share of financing for the project from private sources, rather than REA, demonstrating that cooperatives could raise money in the private capital markets. Buckeye thus obtained a reliable source of power which it continues to use today, and Ohio Power did not have to raise funds to build capacity to serve the cooperatives. Ohio Power also made a small profit on the additional services it provided to the co-op.

Buckeye was forerunner to a new type of G&T cooperative that emerged in the 1970s. Instead of constructing and operating generating capacity themselves, the new G&Ts shared ownership in joint participation projects with other utilities. In many cases their partners were the former power suppliers of their member systems.

Joint participation was attractive to the co-ops for several reasons. It assured a source of power supply at a time when loads were projected to grow rapidly. At that time traditional suppliers, including some investor-owned utilities and government agencies, were expressing concern over their ability to meet the future loads of their wholesale customers. In addition, at a time when wholesale rates were projected to increase rapidly, it gave the cooperative systems a way to control costs. In situations where relations between cooperatives and their investor-owned suppliers had grown increasingly hostile, it also offered the co-ops control over their own resources, rather than continued dependence on a supplier that could use its ownership of power resources for competitive advantage. Several joint action agencies representing municipal utilities became involved in joint participation projects for similar reasons.

At the same time, many investor-owned utilities had large financial commitments to generation under construction. Nuclear projects, in particular, were experiencing massive cost overruns. By offering participation in a project to its wholesale customers (including co-ops), the utility could obtain a large infusion of needed cash while maintaining a high degree of control over transmission and operations. Further, nuclear projects were subject to an antitrust review by the

Department of Justice and the Nuclear Regulatory Commission (successor to the Atomic Energy Commission) as a condition of receiving a commercial operating license. The threat of lengthy antitrust litigation helped many utilities see the value of negotiation. Finally, in some cases there was probably a competitive impetus: a cooperative basing its power supply on current investments in new coal and/or nuclear capacity was unlikely to be a competitive threat to an investor-owned utility offering service at an embedded cost much lower than the incremental cost of new capacity.

In a typical joint participation project, one company takes the lead in constructing the plant for two or more owners. In the early days of joint participation between cooperatives and other utilities, the lead company was usually the investor-owned utility. As the new G&Ts obtained experience, some chose to become the lead participant for new projects or to develop projects on their own. Each owner is responsible for financing its share of the project and shares in the plant's output in proportion to its financial investment—or as otherwise agreed. The lead participant often operates the unit and provides backup services, supplemental power, and transmission services to the other participants.

For example, in one of the first joint participation projects, Oglethorpe Power Corporation, headquartered in Tucker, Georgia, acquired a 30 percent ownership interest in Georgia Power Company's Hatch nuclear plant. The Municipal Electric Authority of Georgia and the city of Dalton, Georgia, also became participants. Georgia Power served as the lead participant. Based on the success of the Hatch project, Oglethorpe obtained participation in other Georgia Power-initiated projects, including 30 percent shares of the Wansley coal plant, the Vogtle nuclear plant, and a combustion turbine, as well as a 60 percent share of units 1 and 2 of the Scherer nuclear plant. The G&T developed a small hydro project on the Oconee River on its own.

Not all cooperatives were so successful. Wabash Valley Power Association, for example, filed for bankruptcy protection after Public Service Company of Indiana, the lead participant in the Marble Hill Nuclear Station, unilaterally stopped construction. Wabash had invested $467 million in the project at the time construction was terminated.

In many cases, however, joint participation helped the cooperatives achieve their goals of securing control of an adequate source of power supply at a reasonable cost.

CHAPTER 7

THE ROLE OF THE FEDERAL GOVERNMENT IN POWER GENERATION

Cooperatives continue to purchase a significant portion of their power requirements from other segments of the industry. In 1993, RUS borrowers generated 157.4 million MWH, or 52.8 percent of their total needs. They purchased an additional 141 million MWH, including 60 million MWH, or 20.1 percent, from privately-owned suppliers,[1] and 81 million MWH, or 19.4 percent, from federal agencies.

Overall, the federal power systems provided about 8 percent of the nation's energy requirements in 1994. When these projects were built, however, the generation of electricity was not the primary purpose. Power generation became a way to pay for projects that were designed to control floods, improve navigation, and conserve water resources.

The Tennessee Valley Authority

Flood control and navigation—not electric generation—were the primary objectives of the Tennessee Valley projects, which began during World War I. During the early 20th Century, the Tennessee River experienced severe periodic flooding, and a series of shoals at Muscle Shoals, Alabama blocked barge traffic. Congress passed the Tennessee Valley Authority Act in May 1933 and placed the activities of various government agencies under the control of the Tennessee Valley Authority (TVA). TVA promptly began a massive program of building dams and flood control projects, which included hydroelectric generating stations. The law authorized TVA to construct power lines to serve farms and small towns that did not have access to electricity at reasonable rates. It also authorized TVA to give **preference** in the sale of power to cooperative organizations as well as public systems, primarily municipalities. This established an important precedent for electric cooperatives and encouraged the growth of both co-ops and municipal utilities.

The production of power from hydroelectric plants depends on the flow of water. In TVA's case, that flow is regulated to meet navigation and flood control needs, not power needs. Over time, TVA built other types of generating plants to back up the hydro facilities. It is the only federal agency which supplies all of the power requirements in its service area.

---

[1]*Includes five cooperatives that have repaid all of their RUS debt. These systems provided 12.0 million MWH, or 4.1 percent of total requirements.*

FIGURE 7.1. Energy Generated and Purchased by REA Borrowers, by Type of Supplier

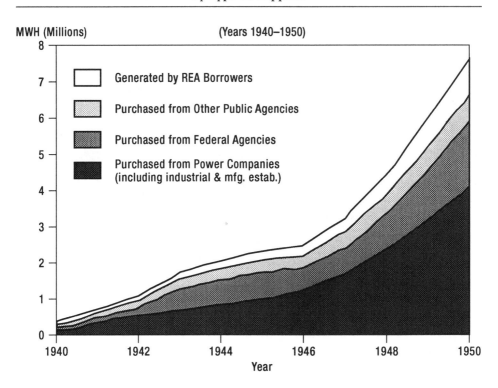

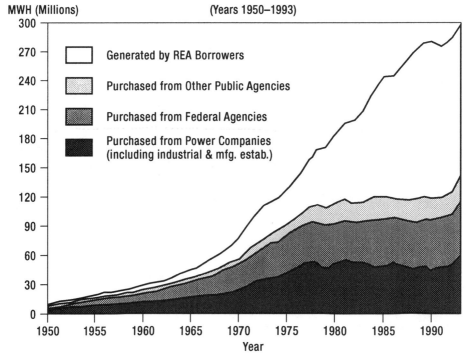

SOURCE: *Rural Electrification Administration, 1993*

THE PREFERENCE CLAUSE

The preference clause gives preference in the sale of power from federal dams to publicly owned and nonprofit utilities. The principle is based on the concept that public resources should be used for the public good and should not be monopolized to benefit private entities. It was first applied to publicly owned systems, such as municipals, in the Reclamation Act of 1902, prior to the advent of rural electric cooperatives.

The preference clause was expanded to include cooperative systems with the TVA Act and has been maintained in the subsequent development of the power marketing administrations. In the rural electric program it has been instrumental in the organization of many cooperative systems and has provided a valuable source of power supply. It provides a useful yardstick for rates and helps to preserve alternative forms of power supply.

TVA, headquartered in Knoxville, Tennessee, is governed by a three-member board of directors appointed by the president and confirmed by the Senate. Directors are appointed for staggered, nine-year terms, and the president appoints one as chairman. In fiscal year 1994, the TVA system, through its retailers, served over seven million consumers, 11 federal agencies, and 160 municipal and cooperative distributors in more than 80,000 square miles in parts of seven states. It operated three nuclear units, 11 coal-fired plants, and 29 hydroelectric plants for a total capacity of 25,924 MW. Total TVA electric sales in fiscal year 1994 were 122.6 billion Kwh, including 102.4 billion Kwh to municipal and cooperative utilities. These local electric systems supply power to most of the region's business and industry as well as to residential and other consumers.

Through major interties with neighboring electric power companies, TVA is constantly buying, selling, and exchanging power. In recent years, the agency has also significantly increased its purchases of power from cogeneration and other small power production facilities.

Cooperatives and municipal systems purchase power from TVA under a contract that is very closely controlled by TVA. The contract specifies that TVA agrees to furnish electric power at a rate which is a combined **demand** and **energy charge**. In return, the distributor agrees to accept certain regulations imposed by the contract. In essence, no profit on the sale of electricity can be used to finance general municipal operations. If the distributor is a municipality, the electric department may pay certain amounts to substitute for taxes to the municipality. The TVA power distributor further agrees that any revenues over and above the cost of operation must be used first to improve the electric distribution system and to pay off local indebtedness in advance. After these conditions are met, the distributor must reduce rates to consumers so that there will be little or no excess revenues over expenses.

As a government entity, TVA pays the states and counties in which it operates in lieu of taxes. In fiscal year 1994, TVA paid $248 million to state and local governments, making TVA the largest taxpayer in Tennessee and one of the largest in Alabama.

TVA is required by law to be self-supporting with revenues from power sales. However, TVA's nonutility economic development activities are funded primarily by appropriations from Congress. In fiscal year 1994, TVA made payments to the U.S. Treasury totaling $42 million for repayment and return on federal appropriations for TVA power facilities. Since 1989, the capital needs of the power program have been funded by the issuance of bonds backed by power revenues, not the federal government.

The TVA programs have had significant success in many areas. Since the dams were completed, there has been no major flood damage on the Tennessee River. Traffic on the river has increased from 33 million ton-miles in 1933 to several billion ton-miles today. The availability of low-cost electricity has promoted economic development which in turn has improved the quality of life and living standards of residents in the Tennessee Valley. TVA's success led to efforts to establish a Missouri Valley Authority, a Columbia River Authority, and an Arkansas Valley Authority. These efforts were not successful.

In 1995, TVA took an aggressive and competitive stance in the electricity market. TVA, while waiting to get approval to do business outside of its normal service territory, is aggressively pursuing potential loads and meeting with customers (Alabama Power customers) in order to get its foot in the door. At this writing, the effectiveness of TVA's plan remains to be seen but its presence is definitely felt in Alabama.

The Federal Power Marketing Administrations

The Flood Control Act of 1944 gave the Secretary of the Interior the authority to create permanent marketing agencies to market the power generated by federal multi-purpose water projects. The secretary "shall transmit and dispose of such power and energy in such manner as to encourage the most widespread use thereof at the lowest possible rates to consumers consistent with sound business principles...." The law also gave preference in the sale of the power and energy to public bodies and cooperatives. The federal government established five power marketing administrations (PMAs) to market the power generated at 133 federal dams. There are significant differences in the operations and responsibilities of the PMAs. Each organization was designed and has evolved to meet the individual needs of the area it serves. In 1977, the Department of Energy Organization Act transferred these responsibilities to the Secretary of Energy.

Bonneville Power Administration. In 1925, Congress ordered a survey of the Columbia River in order to formulate plans for developing the river for navigation, irrigation, and flood control. The survey proposed a series of 10 dams on the Columbia and Snake rivers, and its recommendations became the basis for a wide-ranging regional plan for water conservation, job creation, and industrial development.

FIGURE 7.2. Physical Characteristics of PMAs in 1993

Physical Characteristics	BPA	WAPA	SWPA	SEPA	APA
Generating Capacity marketed* (Mw)	23,286	10,629	2,158	3,092	108
Powerplants*	30	55	24	22	2
Transmission lines operated and maintained (miles)	14,798	16,691	1,382	none	88
Substations	395	271	24	none	5
Power marketed— FY1994 (billions of Kwhs)	87.2	33.1	5.3	5.3	0.4

* *Plants owned by the Federal Government and operated primarily by the U.S. Army Corps of Engineers and the Bureau of Reclamation. Power production is marketed by the PMAs. BPA capacity figure includes 1,100 MW of thermal capacity (primarily nuclear).*

SOURCE: *Congressional Research Service, 1994*

Congress created the Bonneville Power Administration (BPA) in 1937 to sell and deliver the power from the Bonneville and Grand Coulee dams. The potential for power production from Bonneville and Grand Coulee, together with the other proposed dams, was tremendous. BPA, headquartered in Portland, Oregon, has since developed into an extensive public power system that, unlike the other PMAs, has a utility obligation to serve. BPA provides service to 138 customers, including 56 cooperatives. Revenues during 1994 totaled $2.2 billion.

BPA is the marketing and transmission agency for 23,286 MW of capacity owned and operated by the U.S. Army Corps of Engineers and the Bureau of Reclamation as well as power from nonfederal hydro and thermal plants. It operates almost 15,000 circuit miles of high-voltage transmission lines. The system primarily covers parts of four states—Washington, Oregon, Montana, and Idaho—and some adjoining portions of four other states.

BPA's power revenues are used to recover expenses, to repay the federal investment in the power system, and to pay for the resources it has acquired. Power customers must also pay for the investment in irrigation and other non-power facilities to the extent that those users are unable to pay full costs. Like TVA, BPA repays the U.S. Treasury for the taxpayers' investment in river projects. It also covers operation and maintenance expenses at dams and facilities operated by the U.S. Army Corps of Engineers, the Bureau of Reclamation, and the U.S. Fish and Wildlife Service. During 1993, that payment amounted to $730 million.

The Pacific Northwest Electric Power Planning and Conservation Act of 1980, also known as the Pacific Northwest Power Act, had a major impact on BPA. The law holds BPA responsible for meeting the future power needs of the region's utilities.

FIGURE 7 3. Power Marketing Administrations

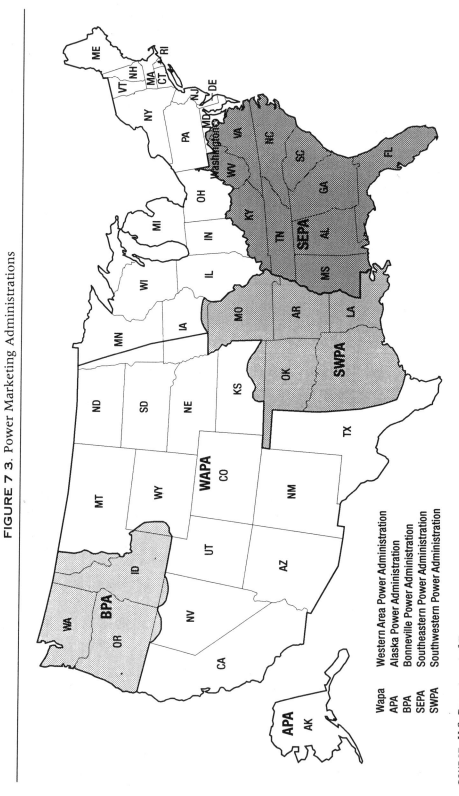

Wapa   Western Area Power Administration
APA   Alaska Power Administration
BPA   Bonneville Power Administration
SEPA   Southeastern Power Administration
SWPA   Southwestern Power Administration

SOURCE: *U.S. Department of Energy*

Prior to the law, BPA simply sold whatever power was available from the federal dams and several other sources. The agency is now authorized to fulfill power needs by acquiring new resources. The Act also gave the agency the role of protecting fish and wildlife in the Columbia River Basin. The Northwest Power Planning Council was formed as a result of that legislation. This independent nonfederal body of eight members—two each from the four main states—works closely with BPA on power supply and environmental issues.

Southwestern Power Administration. The Southwestern Power Administration (SWPA), headquartered in Tulsa, Oklahoma, was created in 1943 by the Secretary of the Interior under the President's war powers and became a permanent agency after passage of the Flood Control Act of 1944. SWPA serves a territory of about 300,000 square miles, including portions of Arkansas, Missouri, Kansas, Oklahoma, Louisiana, and Texas. However, the region did not have the natural resources for hydroelectric development on the same level as TVA and BPA. A total of 2,158 MW of power are available from the 24 hydroelectric plants within the SWPA jurisdiction. SWPA operates 1,382 miles of transmission line to serve 96 customers, including 11 cooperatives.

In addition to the power generated by federal facilities, SWPA transmits and sells supplemental power purchased from public and private utilities under a congressional mandate to encourage widespread, economical use of electric power. It negotiates and administers contracts for the sale of electric power on a wholesale basis and maintains a high-voltage transmission system to serve contractual loads and maintain reliable interconnections. Excess transmission capacity is provided to other utilities in the region.

Southeastern Power Administration. The Southeastern Power Administration (SEPA), headquartered in Elberton, Georgia, was created in 1950 to market power in 10 states: Alabama, Florida, Georgia, Kentucky, Mississippi, North Carolina, South Carolina, Tennessee, Virginia, and West Virginia. SEPA provides power to 272 customers, including 113 cooperatives, from 24 power plants totaling 2,158 MW at reservoir projects operated by the U.S. Army Corps of Engineers. SEPA is not, however, able to provide the full power requirements of its preference customers, who contract on their own for their remaining power needs. SEPA does not own transmission facilities. It must contract with other utilities for the delivery of power to its customers.

Alaska Power Administration. The Alaska Power Administration (APA), headquartered in Juneau, Alaska, was created in 1967 to administer facilities constructed at Eklutna by the Bureau of Reclamation in the mid-1950s, to meet growing power needs for industrial development, and to provide more reliable power at a reasonable cost. APA markets power from two plants totaling 108 MW to five customers, including two cooperatives. New oil and gas reserves were discovered on the Kenai Peninsula in 1957. These reserves could power new resources at a lower cost than some planned federal hydro facilities, which, as a result, were not developed.

In 1989, APA negotiated agreements for the sale of the Snettisham Project to the state of Alaska and the Eklutna facilities to three major public power utilities. The proposed sale is awaiting congressional approval.

Western Area Power Administration. The Western Area Power Administration (WAPA), headquartered in Golden, Colorado, was established by Congress in 1977 as a part of the Department of Energy Organization Act, which transferred power marketing responsibilities previously managed by the Bureau of Reclamation to WAPA. Its service area covers 1.3 million square miles in 15 western states: Arizona, California, Colorado, Iowa, Kansas, Minnesota, Montana, Nebraska, Nevada, New Mexico, North Dakota, South Dakota, Texas, Utah, and Wyoming. WAPA markets the output of 54 plants totaling 10,082 MW operated by the U.S. Bureau of Reclamation, the U.S. Army Corps of Engineers and the International Boundary and Water Commission. It has more than 600 customers, including 47 cooperatives. WAPA also markets the United States' 547 MW entitlement from the coal-fired Navajo Generating Station.

Privatization Issues

Construction and operation of the power marketing agencies' transmission systems and generating plants are financed through congressional appropriations. The U.S. government investment in each generating project as well as yearly investments in the transmission system must be repaid within a specified time, usually 50 years from the date the facility is placed in service. In recent years there have been a number of proposals to privatize, or sell, the power marketing administrations. Some observers say that federal efforts to foster regional growth through low-cost power are no longer needed and that the profit on the sale of the facilities would help reduce the federal deficit. Cooperative and municipal utilities, on the other hand, do not want to lose access to a valuable resource that provides a significant portion of their power requirements. Purchasing replacement power from another source or purchasing the same power from a new owner could substantially increase costs for many cooperative systems and consumers.

While power from the PMA facilities initially cost more than power from other sources, federal hydropower today is a low-cost source of supply for preference customers. In the case of cooperatives, power from the PMAs has helped offset the cost of serving sparsely settled service areas. The preference customers argue that they have provided extensive financial support for these facilities by paying the cost of operation, the cost of maintenance and upgrades, and debt service, including principal and interest on the debt used to build the facilities. The preference customers' support has provided benefits to others in the form of flood control, transportation, water conservation, irrigation, water supply, and recreation.

If the PMAs are sold, the central issue becomes whether the sale should maximize the gain to the Treasury or protect existing customers. Preference customers have proposed that existing PMA customers be allowed to purchase the assets at a cost equivalent to the present value of the remaining debt payments owed the U.S. Treasury. Others have proposed an auction to the highest bidder.

CHAPTER 8

COGENERATION: A MORE EFFICIENT TECHNOLOGY

As far back as the beginning of this century factories commonly generated their own electricity from the process steam they used and, as recently as 1950, as much as 21 percent of all industrial electricity was generated by the user in a process called **cogeneration**. However, as reliable and cheaper electricity became available from utilities, many industrial users switched to purchased power and the amount of cogenerated power dwindled. By 1980, cogeneration accounted for only about three percent of all electricity produced nationally. As energy costs began to rise and capital costs associated with large scale electric generation began to escalate, cogeneration once again became a subject of interest to large consumers of electricity and to regulators interested in containing rate increases.

Cogeneration is the use of a primary fuel to produce both heat and power. In other words, cogeneration is the simultaneous production of either electrical or mechanical power and useful heat usually in the form of process steam. The concept is to recover and use energy which would otherwise be lost. In many applications, cogeneration can significantly reduce energy costs. It can be used in industry, commercial buildings, hospitals, and large residential complexes.

Which comes first, the electricity or the steam? The cogeneration umbrella covers a variety of methods and technologies. The electricity produced can be used by the industrial company, sold to a local utility, or both. Meanwhile, the steam can be used for heating or manufacturing and then converted into more electricity and steam. Depending on how cogeneration is integrated into a production process, technologies are classified into two groups: topping cycles and bottoming cycles. In the most commonly used topping cycle, power generation takes place first and the steam is extracted at a pressure suitable for the industrial process. In the bottoming cycle, heat from a furnace or boiler is first used for the industrial process and the waste heat is recovered for use in power generation.

The technology selected by a cogenerator depends upon the available fuel sources and specific application requirements. No single technique can be imposed in all situations because conditions vary in different industries and in different parts of the country. Traditional fuel sources for cogeneration include waste heat, waste products, and fossil fuels—particularly natural gas. Cogeneration has been one of the fastest growing markets for the natural gas industry.

FIGURE 8.1. A Typical Congeneration System

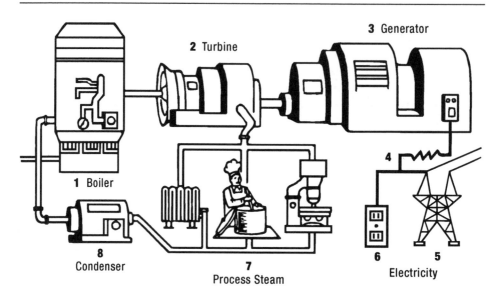

In a typical cogeneration system, fuel burned in a boiler (1) produces steam to drive a turbine (2) that's linked to an electric generator (3). The generator produces electricity (4) that's either sold to a utility (5), used in-house (6), or both. The steam expelled from the turbine is used for heating or manufacturing (7). As the steam cools, either during use or in a condenser (8), it becomes water and is piped back into the boiler.

Reprinted with permission from Cogeneration World.

A cogeneration system generally consists of a thermal energy device such as a boiler, a prime mover (a steam turbine), a generator, and a heat exchanger. Most currently available technologies have been used for many years. New technology in electronics, instrumentation, and mechanics, however, have made modern cogeneration systems more dependable and automatic than models of years past. Commercially available cogeneration systems include steam turbines with flue gas treatment, gas turbines with waste heat exchangers, combined cycles, and diesel engines.

Assembled by a manufacturer, the cogeneration unit must be installed by the buyer. The installation of these systems is site-specific because cogeneration is often retrofitted to the existing industrial process. Many of the most recently installed cogeneration systems use gas turbines and produce more electricity than is required by the industrial firm because the local utility must, under, the Public Utility Regulatory Policies Act of 1978, buy the excess electric power.

The important distinguishing features in comparing relative advantages of cogeneration technologies are the fuels used, the capital investment required, the efficiency in converting the fuel to electricity, the electricity-to-steam ratio, and the environmental effects. Applications for bottoming-cycle cogeneration technologies are limited and their sizes are usually very small. Most industrial or commercial process heat requirements are too low for the reject heat to be used effectively in bottoming-cycle power generation.

Traditional Users of Cogeneration

Industrial cogeneration is by far the most important application of cogeneration. Since cooperatives serve few large industrial consumers, there have been few opportunities for them to participate in cogeneration projects. The four major cogenerating industries are pulp and paper, chemicals, petroleum refining, and primary metals. They all share a need for medium- to high-pressure steam in their industrial processes, which makes them especially suited to utilize the steam energy produced in the generation of electricity.

A great deal of interest in cogeneration has been shown by such institutions as hospitals, hotels, laundries, and universities. This resurgence of interest in cogeneration is due in part to several events. First, the number of sites with suitable thermal loads has increased. Second, the power rates in many areas have risen substantially—a trend that is expected to continue. Third, the availability of more flexible, modular cogeneration systems has increased. And finally, government regulations have changed the cogeneration picture dramatically. By 1993, cogenerators in the U.S. were operating over 43,144 MW of electric capacity.

Cogenerators and Small Power Producers

A cogeneration facility can qualify for benefits under PURPA if it can meet three criteria: the ownership standard, the operating standard, and the efficiency standard. The criteria for each of these standards were determined by FERC. A qualifying cogenerator must be owned by a person not primarily engaged in the generation or sale of electric power other than the power solely cogenerated. Electric utilities may participate in joint ventures, but may own no more than 50 percent of the equity of the qualifying facility. Thus, the primary business of the cogenerator must be for some purpose other than generation of power.

All topping-cycle cogenerators must meet the FERC's operating standard; no operating standard has been prescribed for bottoming-cycle generators. The operating standard is that "the useful thermal energy output of the facility must, during any calendar year, be no less than five percent of the total energy output." Thus, after the electricity has been generated, the steam which is then extracted for some industrial purpose must be of some significance. If that steam constitutes less than five percent of total energy output, it is clearly not significant in terms of the total plant operation.

The efficiency standard applies only to gas- or oil-fired boilers at which the cogeneration facility was installed on or after March 13, 1980. The standard differs somewhat for topping-cycle and bottoming-cycle facilities due to engineering considerations. The efficiency standards are based on fuel cycles and prescribe levels of thermal efficiency for the production of electric power. A facility which cannot produce electric power at an acceptable level of efficiency is not meeting the intent of PURPA.

PURPA ENCOURAGES COGENERATION

The Public Utility Regulatory Policies Act of 1978 was intended to encourage more efficient use of electricity through cogeneration and to promote the use of renewable energy resources. It did this by creating a new class of electric generator, the qualifying facility (QF). QFs include cogeneration facilities and small power producers which meet the standards set forth in the legislation. PURPA requires local utilities to interconnect with QFs, to provide backup power supplies, and to purchase any power generated above the QF's own requirements. (In the alternative, a QF may require the utility to purchase all of its electrical output and to supply the QF's power requirements at the standard retail rate). A 1983 Supreme Court ruling upheld PURPA benefits which require utilities to purchase cogenerated power at "avoided cost"—the cost the utility would have incurred by producing the power itself or purchasing it from another supplier. In the case of a distribution cooperative, the avoided cost has been determined to be the avoided cost of the co-op's power supplier, not the cooperative's cost of purchased power. QFs are exempt from reporting procedures associated with state and FERC utility regulations.

A **small power producer** (SPP) is a facility of no more than 80 MW that uses a renewable resource, such as water, wind, wood, solar energy, geothermal energy, or waste materials, to generate electricity.

The effect of PURPA on the electric utility industry cannot be overemphasized. It guaranteed a market for QF electricity at prices that were determined by regulators to cover the costs of production. On December 31, 1993, there were more than 43,144 MW of cogeneration capacity in operation in the United States, 77.3 percent of which was QF capacity. In addition, 74.5 percent of all cogeneration capacity had been placed in service after the passage of PURPA. SPPs provided an additional 10,516 MW of QF capacity.

THE IPPS EMERGE

In recent years, legislative and regulatory changes have encouraged the development of another generation alternative: **independent power producers** (IPPs)—companies generating electricity through projects which 1) are not constructed or operated as traditional rate regulated generating plants and 2) do not operate as QFs under PURPA. These changes signal a shift from the traditional utility model to a more competitive market environment in which any party may compete to meet new generation needs.

One of the greatest advantages of IPPs is that developers can pursue projects that do not satisfy the legal requirements under PURPA. At the end of 1993, 74 percent of nonutility generation was cogeneration, but there are a limited number of suitable steam hosts to support cogeneration projects, and few of these are in cooperative service territories. A steam host may not be located—or willing to relocate—in an area where a new power project is needed. In addition, the capacity in greatest demand nationwide is peaking capacity—and it is difficult to develop peaking projects as qualifying cogeneration facilities—because hosts' steam requirements often do not coincide with purchasing utility's demand peaks. As recent regulatory changes have made it easier to develop competitive generation without obtaining QF status, interest in new cogeneration projects has waned.

The mechanics of providing electricity are the same throughout the industry. A kilowatt-hour does not know whether it was generated by a cooperative, a municipality, a government agency, an investor-owned utility, or an independent power producer. It does not know whether the parental force that moved a conductor through a magnetic field was steam created by the combustion of coal, oil, or gas; the fissioning of atoms; or falling water. It has no interest in the ownership of the transmission and distribution lines it follows on the way to transforming itself into light, heat, or computing capabilities.

The unique contribution of the rural electric program, then, is not in the performance of any of these activities, but in the way it has developed a strong network of resources to perform them for consumers with characteristics relatively unattractive to electricity suppliers: low density, largely residential loads often situated in difficult areas to serve.

PART 3

ACCOUNTING AND FINANCE

CHAPTER 9

COOPERATIVE APPROACHES TO FINANCE AND ACCOUNTING

"Reliable accounting records are essential to every REA borrower as a basis for proper management of the business enterprise, as a source of information for REA in regard to loan security, and as a vital factor in the successful administration of the whole rural electrification program. In order to be of the greatest value, the records must not only be accurate, but must also be maintained in a uniform manner, thereby furnishing a basis for analysis, comparison, and interpretation."

—REA Borrower Accounting (Electric)
Course Guide, C-ACCT 211
USDA Graduate School

Cooperatives, like other businesses, are required to maintain good accounting records. Such records are a necessary tool of management, helping the board of directors set policy and management maintain reliable, economic operations. Financial data included in the annual report and other communications helps members to understand the value of their participation in the cooperative. If the system is regulated, good records provide the information commissions need to make sound rate decisions. Financial statements to lenders and other creditors demonstrate the cooperative's solvency, creditworthiness, and stability.

Long before there were electric cooperatives and even before the regulatory commissions became involved in accounting records, public utilities themselves recognized the need for a uniform, systematic method of keeping accounts. As early as 1922, the National Association of Railroad and Utilities Commissioners, in conjunction with the national utility company associations, recommended a Uniform Classification of Accounts. The Public Utility Act of 1935, commonly known as the Federal Power Act, gave the Federal Power Commission (FPC) authority to establish a uniform system of accounts for public utilities and licensees subject to the law. Today, that responsibility rests with the Federal Energy Regulatory Commission (FERC), the successor to the FPC.

REA quickly realized that the electric cooperatives would also benefit from uniform accounting procedures and established the REA Uniform System of

Accounts (7 CFR 1767B-1) for rural electric borrowers. The REA system generally conforms to the FERC Uniform System of Accounts, with changes that reflect the nonprofit, cooperative nature of the rural electric systems and their unique financing mechanisms. The accounts show in a manner that is consistent from cooperative to cooperative and for the same cooperative over time:

- the cooperative's revenues, the sources of funds flowing into the business.

- the cooperative's expenses, the cost of operating the business.

- the cooperative's assets, or the costs of the property acquired to do business.

Each account is assigned a number and a descriptive title. While disagreements occur over which account should cover a particular item, the system generally works well to ensure a high degree of consistency and accuracy in co-op records.

FINANCIAL AND STATISTICAL REPORT

The information contained in the Uniform System of Accounts can be organized and summarized to provide reports to aid management in operating and controlling the business. RUS requires each of its borrowers to submit an annual Financial and Statistical Report, which includes a statement of operations and a balance sheet, along with other information. Quarterly reports are required of systems that experienced a deficit in the prior operating year. RUS may also require some systems to report on a monthly basis. To assure uniformity, RUS has prescribed a report form. Distribution systems report on RUS Form 7, while power supply systems and distribution systems with generation report on RUS Form 12. RUS compiles an annual financial and statistical report of all borrowers' electrical operations. It files a copy of the report with FERC, relieving most individual systems of that responsibility. Rural electric systems that are no longer RUS borrowers are required by their lenders to provide similar reports.

The Statement of Operations

The statement of operations filed with RUS shows revenues received, expenses incurred, and net margins and patronage capital during a given period of time. Most cooperatives prepare the report on a monthly basis as a management tool.

As nonprofit organizations, cooperatives are committed by policy to keeping rates as low as possible. Any revenues in excess of operating costs are called net margins and patronage capital. The **net margins** and **patronage capital** are treated as **equity capital** contributed by the cooperative's members, and eventually must be returned to the members in proportion to their patronage, or purchase of electricity. Another name for patronage capital is **capital credits**. Patronage capital is usually retained by the cooperative for a number of years before it is refunded to the members, assuming financial conditions permit.

Figure 9.1 shows Parts A through D of a typical financial and statistical report for a distribution system. Parts E through R (not shown) contain details of the data summarized in Parts A through D. The statement of operations is shown in Part

A. The cost of power (Line 3) represents 65.5 percent of operating revenues and patronage capital (Line 1), while interest on long-term debt (Line 15) represents less than 5 percent of operating revenues and patronage capital.

As noted, the patronage capital (Line 28) is retained by the co-op and is available for use for a number of years for such things as maintenance and improvements. In addition, depreciation is a bookkeeping expense which does not require a current cash payment. Thus, the net margins and patronage capital plus depreciation show the amount of cash generated during the period, or cash flow.

> Net Margin and Patronage Capital + Depreciation = Cash Flow

In addition to the revenues received from the sale of electricity, many cooperatives also receive non-operating margins, or revenues from activities unrelated to electricity sales. These might include interest on investments or cash from the sale of property. Cooperatives that are members of G&Ts may receive patronage capital allocations from the G&T. However, cash distributions of G&T capital credits are rare. G&Ts usually retain this money for their own needs. Allocations show up as assets on distribution co-op books.

Figure 9.2 shows RUS Form 12a of a financial and statistical report for a typical G&T cooperative. Parts 12b through 12i (not shown) provide additional details of the data summarized on Form 12a. G&Ts that purchase power from other G&Ts may also receive patronage capital allocations. Debt represents a much higher percentage of operating revenues and patronage capital than for distribution systems—more than 20 percent—because of large investments in high cost plants and lines.

The Balance Sheet

The **balance sheet** is a statement of the cooperative's financial position at a particular time, often the last day of the year. Most cooperatives also update the balance sheet on a monthly basis, in addition to preparing the year-end report required by RUS and other lenders.

The balance sheet shows the cooperative's total **capitalization**, or the total dollar value of the capital used by the business. The term capital refers to the manmade goods and natural resources used in the operation of a business enterprise. For convenience, capital is usually expressed in terms of money. In this sense, it means the dollars invested in the cooperative by its members, lenders, and others.

The balance sheet compares the system's total assets and other debits, or the property and investments it owns, with its total liabilities and other credits, or the

FIGURE 9.1. Financial and Statistical Report

Exhibit A

Public reporting burden for this collection of information is estimated to average 17 hours per response, including the time for reviewing instructions, searching existing data sources, gathering and maintaining the data needed, and completing and reviewing the collection of information. Send comments regarding this burden estimate or any other aspect of this collection of information, including suggestions for reducing this burden, to Department of Agriculture, Clearance Officer, OIRM, AG Box 7630, Washington, DC 20250; and to the Office of Management and Budget, Paperwork Reduction Project (OMB #0572- 0032), Washington, DC 20503. OMB FORM NO. 0572-0032, Expires 03/31/95.

This data will be used by REA to review your financial situation. Your response is required (7 U.S.C. 901 et seq.) and is not confidential.

USDA-REA	BORROWER DESIGNATION US 01
FINANCIAL AND STATISTICAL REPORT	BORROWER NAME AND ADDRESS Rural Area Electric Cooperative, Inc.
INSTRUCTIONS - *Submit an original and two copies to REA. Round all amounts to nearest dollar. For detailed instructions, see REA Bulletin 1717B-2*	PERIOD ENDED 12-31-94 / REA USE ONLY

CERTIFICATION

We hereby certify that the entries in this report are in accordance with the accounts and other records of the system and reflect the status of the system to the best of our knowledge and belief.

ALL INSURANCE REQUIRED BY PART 1788 OF 7 CFR CHAPTER XVII, REA, WAS IN FORCE DURING THE REPORTING PERIOD AND RENEWALS HAVE BEEN OBTAINED FOR ALL POLICIES

SIGNATURE OF OFFICE MANAGER OR ACCOUNTANT   DATE

SIGNATURE OF MANAGER   DATE

PART A. STATEMENT OF OPERATIONS

ITEM	LAST YEAR (a)	THIS YEAR (b)	BUDGET (c)	THIS MONTH (d)
1. Operating Revenue and Patronage Capital		18,269,576		
2. Power Production Expense		0		
3. Cost of Purchased Power		11,978,727		
4. Transmission Expense		0		
5. Distribution Expense - Operation		443,816		
6. Distribution Expense - Maintenance		779,867		
7. Customer Accounts Expense		450,087		
8. Customer Service and Informational Expense		92,934		
9. Sales Expense		0		
10. Administrative and General Expense		1,152,433		
11. Total Operation & Maintenance Expense (2 thru 10)		14,897,864		
12. Depreciation and Amortization Expense		1,016,615		
13. Tax Expense - Property and Gross Receipts		245,069		
14. Tax Expense - Other		234,960		
15. Interest on Long-Term Debt		884,943		
16. Interest Charged to Construction - Credit	( )	(0)	( )	( )
17. Interest Expense - Other		0		
18. Other Deductions		94,417		
19. Total Cost of Electric Service (11 thru 18)		17,373,868		
20. Patronage Capital & Operating Margins (1 minus 19)		895,708		
21. Non-Operating Margins - Interest		143,075		
22. Allowance for Funds Used During Construction		0		
23. Income (Loss) from Equity Investments		0		
24. Non-Operating Margins - Other		0		
25. Generation and Transmission Capital Credits		222,111		
26. Other Capital Credits and Patronage Dividends		101,313		
27. Extraordinary Items		0		
28. Patronage Capital or Margins (20 thru 27)		1,362,207		

PART B. DATA ON TRANSMISSION AND DISTRIBUTION PLANT

ITEM	LAST YEAR (a)	THIS YEAR (b)	ITEM	LAST YEAR (a)	THIS YEAR (b)
1. New Services Connected			5. Miles Transmission		
2. Services Retired			6. Miles Distribution - Overhead		
3. Total Services in Place			7. Miles Distribution - Underground		
4. Idle Services (Exclude Seasonal)			8. Total Miles Energized (5 + 6 + 7)		

REA Form 7   *(Rev. 12-93)*   **FACSIMILE**   Page 1 of 7 Pages

FIGURE 9.1. Financial and Statistical Report

USDA-REA	BORROWER DESIGNATION	
FINANICAL AND STATISTICAL REPORT	US01	REA USE ONLY
	PERIOD ENDED	
INSTRUCTIONS - *See REA Bulletin 1717B-2*	12-31-94	

PART C. BALANCE SHEET

ASSETS AND OTHER DEBITS		LIABILITIES AND OTHER CREDITS	
1. Total Utility Plant in Service	35,361,090	30. Memberships	122,050
2. Construction Work in Progress	845,250	31. Patronage Capital	8,164,922
3. Total Utility Plant (1 + 2)	36,206,340	32. Operating Margins - Prior Years	2,831,851
4. Accum. Provision for Depreciation and Amort.	9,687,670	33. Operating Margins - Current Year	1,681,861
5. Net Utility Plant (3 - 4)	26,518,670	34. Non-Operating Margins	1,106,866
6. Non-Utility Property (Net)	0	35. Other Margins and Equities	589,370
7. Investments in Subsidiary Companies	0	36. Total Margins & Equities (30 thru 35)	14,496,920
8. Invest. In Assoc. Org. - Patronage Capital	1,035,366	37. Long-Term Debt - REA (Net)	12,450,180
9. Invest. In Assoc. Org. - Other - General Funds	0	(Payments-Unapplied $ _____)	
10. Invest. In Assoc. Org. - Other - Nongeneral Funds	2,415,854	38. Long-Term Debt - REA - Econ. Devel. (Net)	0
11. Investments in Economic Development Projects	0	39. Long-Term Debt - Other - REA Guaranteed.	0
12. Other Investments	10,000	40. Long-Term Debt - Other (Net)	5,209,650
13. Special Funds	434,180	41. Total Long -Term Debt (37 thru 40)	17,659,830
14. Total Other Property and Investments (6 thru 13)	3,895,400	42. Obligations Under Capital Leases	0
15. Cash - General Funds	678,890	43. Accumulated Operating Provisions	113,670
16. Cash - Construction Funds - Trustee	0	44. Total Other Noncurrent Liabilities (42 + 43)	113,670
17. Special Deposits	0	45. Notes Payable	0
18. Temporary Investments	905,186	46. Accounts Payable	1,372,724
19. Notes Receivable (Net)	0	47. Consumers Deposits	57,614
20. Accounts Receivable - Sales of Energy (Net)	1,860,157	48. Other Current and Accrued Liabilities	1,074,632
21. Accounts Receivable - Other (Net)	9,052	49. Total Current & Accrued Liabilities (45 thru 48)	2,504,970
22. Materials and Supplies - Electric and Other	905,186	50. Deferred Credits	726,060
23. Prepayments	135,778	51. Accumulated Deferred Income Taxes	0
24. Other Current and Accrued Assets	31,681	52. Total Liabilities and Other Credits	
25. Total Current and Accrued Assets (15 thru 24)	4,525,930	(36 + 41 + 44 + 49 thru 51)	35,501,450
26. Regulatory Assets	0	ESTIMATED CONTRIBUTIONS IN AID OF CONSTRUCTION	
27. Other Deferred Debits	561,450	53. Balance Beginning of Year	
28. Accumulated Deferred Income Taxes	0	54. Amount Received This Year (Net)	
29. Total Assets and Other Debits (5+14+25 thru 28)	35,501,450	55. Total Contributions in Aid of Construction	

PART D. NOTES TO FINANCIAL STATEMENTS

THIS SPACE BELOW IS PROVIDED FOR IMPORTANT NOTES REGARDING THE FINANCIAL STATEMENT CONTAINED IN THIS REPORT.
(IF ADDITIONAL SPACE IS NEEDED, USE SEPARATE SHEET.)

REA Form 7 *(Rev. 12-93)*	**FACSIMILE**	Page 2 of 7 Pages

FIGURE 9.2. Operating Report—Financial

Exhibit A

Public reporting burden for this collection of information is estimated to average 24.25 hours (REA Form 12a-i) per response, including the time for reviewing instructions, searching existing data sources, gathering and maintaining the data needed, and completing and reviewing the collection of information. Send comments regarding this burden estimate or any other aspect of this collection of information, including suggestions for reducing this burden, to Department of Agriculture, Clearance Officer, OIRM, AG Box 7630, Washington, DC 20250; and to the Office of Management and Budget, Paperwork Reduction Project (OMB #0572- 0017), Washington, DC 20503. OMB FORM NO. 0572-0017, Expires 12/31/94.

This data will be used by REA to review your financial situation. Your response is required (7 U.S.C. 901 et seq.) and is not confidential.

USDA-REA	BORROWER DESIGNATION US 50
OPERATING REPORT - FINANCIAL	BORROWER NAME AND ADDRESS Rural G & T Cooperative, Inc.
INSTRUCTIONS - *Submit an original and two copies to REA. Round all amounts to nearest dollar. For detailed instructions, see REA Bulletin 1717B-3*	PERIOD ENDED 12-31-94 REA USE ONLY

CERTIFICATION

We hereby certify that the entries in this report are in accordance with the accounts and other records of the system and reflect the status of the system to the best of our knowledge and belief.

ALL INSURANCE REQUIRED BY PART 1788 OF 7 CFR CHAPTER XVII, REA, WAS IN FORCE DURING THE REPORTING PERIOD AND RENEWALS HAVE BEEN OBTAINED FOR ALL POLICIES.

SIGNATURE OF OFFICE MANAGER OR ACCOUNTANT	DATE
SIGNATURE OF MANAGER	DATE

SECTION A. STATEMENT OF OPERATIONS

ITEM	LAST YEAR (a)	YEAR-TO-DATE THIS YEAR (b)	BUDGET (c)	THIS MONTH (d)
1. Electric Energy Revenues		206,271,787		
2. Income From Leased Property (Net)		0		
3. Other Operating Revenue and Income		465,963		
4. Total Oper. Revenues & Patronage Capital *(1 thru 3)*		206,737,750		
5. Operating Expense - Production - Excluding Fuel		5,989,891		
6. Operating Expense - Production - Fuel		65,930,237		
7. Operating Expense - Other Power Supply		50,102,667		
8. Operating Expense - Transmission		287,820		
9. Operating Expense - Distribution		612,113		
10. Operating Expense - Customer Accounts		587,621		
11. Operating Expense - Customer Service & Information		36,219		
12. Operating Expense - Sales		0		
13. Operating Expense - Administrative & General		6,039,720		
14. Total Operation Expense *(5 thru 13)*		129,586,288		
15. Maintenance Expense - Production		7,941,805		
16. Maintenance Expense - Transmission		221,620		
17. Maintenance Expense - Distribution		660,244		
18. Maintenance Expense - General Plant		882,422		
19. Total Maintenance Expense *(15 thru 18)*		9,706,091		
20. Depreciation and Amortization Expense		18,056,200		
21. Taxes		4,462,440		
22. Interest on Long-Term Debt		40,295,481		
23. Interest Charged to Construction - Credit	( )	(54,753)	( )	( )
24. Other Interest Expense		0		
25. Other Deductions		3,698,040		
26. Total Cost of Electric Service *(14 + 19 thru 25)*		205,749,787		
27. Operating Margins *(4 less 26)*		987,963		
28. Interest Income		248,221		
29. Allowance For Funds Used During Construction		0		
30. Income (Loss) from Equity Investments		0		
31. Other Nonoperating Income (Net)		0		
32. Generation & Transmission Capital Credits		956,760		
33. Other Capital Credits and Patronage Dividends		75,888		
34. Extraordinary Items		0		
35. Net Patronage Capital or Margins *(27 thru 34)*		2,268,832		

ITEM	Mills/kWh *(Optional Use by Borrower)*		
36. Electric Energy Revenue per kWh Sold			
37. Total Operation & Maintenance Expense Per kWh Sold			
38. Total Cost of Electric Service per kWh Sold			
39. Purchase Power Cost Per kWh Sold			

REA Form **12a**   *(Rev. 12-93)*

FACSIMILE

FIGURE 9.2. Operating Report—Financial

USDA-REA	BORROWER DESIGNATION	
	US50	
OPERATING REPORT - FINANCIAL	PERIOD ENDED	REA USE ONLY
	12-31-94	

SECTION B. BALANCE SHEET

ASSETS AND OTHER DEBITS		LIABILITIES AND OTHER CREDITS	
1. Total Utility Plant in Service	644,818,520	32. Memberships	5,040
2. Construction Work in Progress	29,397,640	33. Patronage Capital	
3. Total Utility Plant *(1 + 2)*	674,216,160	a. Assigned and Assignable	8,516,900
4. Accum. Provision for Depreciation and Amort.	198,730,560	b. Retired This Year	0
5. Net Utility Plant *(3 − 4)*	475,485,600	c. Retired Prior Years	125,000
6. Non-Utility Property (Net)	1,980,901	d. Net Patronage Capital	8,641,900
7. Investments in Subsidiary Companies	15,986,186	34. Operating Margins - Prior Years	0
8. Invest. In Assoc. Org. - Patronage Capital	7,428,332	35. Operating Margins - Current Year	2,246,832
9. Invest. In Assoc. Org. - Other - General Funds	0	36. Non-Operating Margins	0
10. Invest. In Assoc. Org. - Other - Nongeneral Funds	12,430,888	37. Other Margins and Equities	0
11. Investments in Economic Development Projects	0	38. Total Margins & Equities *(32 + 33d thru 37)*	10,893,772
12. Other Investments	17,828,115	39. Long-Term Debt - REA (Net)	110,249,730
13. Special Funds	2,200,980	(Payments-Unapplied $ _____)	
14. Total Other Property and Investments *(6 thru 13)*	57,855,400	40. Long-Term Debt - REA - Econ. Devel. (Net).	392,069,470
15. Cash - General Funds	85,839	41. Long-Term Debt - FFB - REA Guaranteed	0
16. Cash - Construction Funds - Trustee	0	42. Long-Term Debt - Other - REA Guaranteed.	0
17. Special Deposits	0	43. Long-Term Debt - Other (Net)	68,253,600
18. Temporary Investments	39,375,130	44. Total Long -Term Debt *(39 thru 43)*	570,572,800
19. Notes Receivable (Net)	0	45. Obligations Under Capital Leases - Noncurrent	0
20. Accounts Receivable - Sales of Energy (Net)	17,189,316	46. Accumulated Operating Provisions	60,688,540
21. Accounts Receivable - Other (Net)	0	47. Total Other Noncurrent Liabilities *(45 + 46)*	60,688,540
22. Fuel Stock	16,482,559	48. Notes Payable	0
23. Materials and Supplies - Other	12,559,416	49. Accounts Payable	15,788,974
24. Prepayments	0	50. Taxes Accrued	0
25. Other Current and Accrued Assets	2,245,232	51. Interest Accrued	0
26. Total Current and Accrued Assets *(15 thru 25)*	87,937,492	52. Other Current and Accrued Liabilities	7,919,666
27. Unamortized Debt Discount & Extraor. Prop. Losses	0	53. Total Current & Accrued Liabilities *(48 thru 52)*	23,708,640
28. Regulatory Assets	0	54. Deferred Credits	36,992,320
29. Other Deferred Debits	81,577,580	55. Accumulated Deferred Income Taxes	0
30. Accumulated Deferred Income Taxes	0	56. Total Liabilities and Other Credits	
31. Total Assets and Other Debits *(5+14+26 thru 30)*	702,856,072	*(38 + 44 + 47 + 53 thru 55)*	702,856,072

SECTION C. NOTES TO FINANCIAL STATEMENTS

THIS SPACE BELOW IS PROVIDED FOR IMPORTANT NOTES REGARDING THE FINANCIAL STATEMENT CONTAINED IN THIS REPORT.
(IF ADDITIONAL SPACE IS NEEDED, USE SEPARATE SHEET.)

REA Form **12a**   *(Rev. 12-93)*

FACSIMILE

amounts it owes to others. The difference (assets minus liabilities) is the cooperative's **equity**, or net worth. Equity includes memberships, patronage capital, and other equities, such as non-refundable donations or contributions for construction purposes. By convention, assets are shown on the left side of the balance sheet, while liabilities, including equities, are shown on the right side.

Assets − Liabilities = Net Worth

The assets show how the cooperative's capital was invested on the day covered by the balance sheet. Asset accounts are generally divided into **fixed assets**, including plant and equipment, and current assets, including cash, accounts receivable, and materials and supplies. **Current assets** are those used in day-to-day operations or amounts collectible within a short period of time, usually a year.

The **liabilities** show how the cooperative's capital was raised. Long-term liabilities are primarily long-term debt from RUS and other lenders, while current liabilities include bills and short-term debt which must be repaid within a short period of time, usually a year.

The term **capital structure** relates to the proportion of debt and equity shown on the balance sheet, which represents the capitalization of a company. Looking at the balance sheets shown in Figures 9.1 and 9.2, the most obvious difference in the capital structure of the distribution system and the G&T is in the equity level. Collectively in 1993, the electric distribution systems had a composite equity level of 40.8 percent while the power supply systems had a composite equity level of 1.2 percent.

Historically, G&Ts have relied on the financial strength of their member systems and their relationships with them through the wholesale power contract to demonstrate financial stability. This reflects a conscious decision on the part of the program. Since its members are the only source of equity a cooperative has, it has been impractical for most G&Ts to accumulate a large equity base. The G&Ts require much larger dollar amounts for investments in transmission and generation than do the distribution systems. The rates to member systems would have to be higher than they are today in order for most G&Ts to accumulate a significant level of equity.

Under the wholesale power contract, the distribution system agrees to purchase all of its power requirements from the G&T. It further agrees to pay rates that, combined with the G&T's other sources of revenue, will be sufficient to pay all the G&T's expenses. The rates are subject to approval by RUS and, in some cases, a regulatory authority. The G&T's board of directors is required to review the rates at least once a year.

The wholesale power contract provides the G&T with a guaranteed source of revenue to pay its debts. Thus, G&T systems have been able to obtain attractive debt financing from RUS and other lenders without building a high equity level.

In recent years, however, doubts have arisen about whether RUS will be able to supply adequate funding to meet G&T needs in the future. As a result, some G&Ts are looking at building higher equity levels as a way of positioning themselves to attract new sources of financing. This approach may be impractical for systems which already have relatively high rates.

EVALUATING COOPERATIVE FINANCIAL PERFORMANCE

Historically, a cooperative's financial performance has been evaluated on the basis of its equity level, Times Interest Earned Ratio (TIER), and Debt Service Coverage Ratio (DSC). TIER is a key measure of a cooperative's financial health and its ability to meet interest expense on long-term debt.

The 1970 REA common mortgage requires a distribution borrower to achieve an average TIER of 1.5 for two of the last three years. Power supply borrowers are required to achieve an average TIER of 1.00 for two of the last three years. (In some cases, RUS has required G&Ts to meet a 1.05 TIER standard as a condition of approval of special financings.) If the borrower does not meet this standard, then financing is not available to them.

DSC provides another way of measuring ability to make debt service payments. The original RUS common mortgage requires a distribution borrower to achieve an average DSC of 1.25 for the two highest of the last three years. Power supply borrowers are required to achieve an average DSC of 1.00 for the two highest of the last three years.

At one time, a distribution system was required to achieve a 40 percent equity level in order to refund patronage capital. In recent years, RUS has relaxed its emphasis on building equity and placed more on the need for adequate cash flows from utility operations to repay debt. In July 1995, RUS adopted a new mortgage and published proposed rules for new loan documents in the Federal Register. The new policies shift the financial performance requirements from the mortgage to the loan documents and establish requirements for Operating TIER (OTIER) and Operating DSC for co-ops, (ODSC) for distribution systems. OTIER and ODSC exclude major non-cash margins, such as patronage capital allocations from G&Ts, and thus more clearly reflect the cooperative's cash position. Under the new documents, which will be phased in, distribution systems will be required to achieve an average OTIER and ODSC of 1.1 for the two highest of the last three years. The new documents will require G&T systems to meet 1.05 TIER and 1.00 DSC standards. This will mean lower rates for the co-ops by reducing the amount of margins needed to make TIER.

FIGURE 9.3. Criteria for Evaluating Cooperative Creditworthiness

---

Times Interest Earned Ratio (TIER)

$$\text{TIER} = \frac{\text{Patronage Capital and Margins + Interest Expense}}{\text{Interest Expense}}$$

The 1970 REA common mortgage required a distribution system to achieve an average TIER of 1.5 for the two highest of the last three years. For a power supply borrower, the requirement was an average TIER of 1.0 for the two highest of the last three years.

$$\text{Operating TIER (OTIER)} = \frac{\text{Patronage Capital \& Operating Margins of Electric System* + Interest Expense}}{\text{Patronage Capital \& Operating Margins of Electric System}}$$

*Operating revenue and patronage capital of electric system operations less total cost of electric service including interest expense on all long-term debt

RUS has proposed that distribution systems be required to achieve an OTIER of 1.1 for the two best years of the three most recent calendar years.

Debt Service Coverage Ratio (DSC)

$$\text{DSC} = \frac{\text{Patronage Capital and Margins + Interest Expense + Depreciation and Amortization Expense}}{\text{Debt Service Billed}}$$

The 1970 REA common mortgage required a distribution system to achieve an average DSC of 1.25 for the two highest of the last three years. For a power supply borrower, the requirement was an average DSC of 1.00 for the two highest of the last three years.

$$\text{Operating DSC (ODSC)} = \frac{\text{Depreciation and Amortization Expense + Interest Expense + Patronage Capital \& Operating Margins of the Electric System}}{\text{Debt Service Billed}}$$

RUS has proposed that distribution systems be required to achieve an ODSC of 1.1 for the two best years of the three most recent calendar years.

$$\text{Modified DSC} = \frac{\text{Patronage Capital and Operating Margins + Interest Expense + Depreciation and Amortization Expense + Cash Patronage Capital Retirements Received}}{\text{Debt Service Billed}}$$

CFC has adopted the Modified DSC as a part of its credit analysis.

The National Rural Utilities Cooperative Finance Corporation (CFC) has also adopted new standards for its loans to distribution systems who are not REA borrowers. There is no TIER or equity requirement, but borrowers must achieve an average modified DSC of 1.35 for the two highest of the last three years. These standards are the minimums necessary to meet lender requirements. Most systems try to exceed this performance level. The optimum level depends on many conditions, such as equity level, rate levels compared to neighboring utilities, interest rate on debt, and many other factors. Each system should develop clear financial goals, including target TIER and DSC levels, and a plan for meeting them.

Further analysis of the statement of operations and balance sheet can provide management with additional useful information. A horizontal analysis, or comparison of this year's operating results with last year's, can help identify a potential problem area where expenses may be getting out of hand, or an area in which improvements are being made. For example, a significant increase in distribution maintenance expense could reflect repairs after a storm, which would probably not indicate a cause for concern. If there is no such obvious explanation, however, management needs to find the problem and fix it. A similar analysis can be performed on the balance sheet. A significant increase in materials and supplies, for instance, might raise questions about inventory management.

A vertical analysis, which calculates each expense as a percentage of total revenues for a given time period, highlights the co-op's major expenses.

Both RUS and CFC provide special reports that allow a system to compare itself with others. REA's Borrower Statistical Profile compares a borrower's performance with other co-ops in its state, with the same power supplier, and across the nation. CFC's Key Ratio Trend Analysis ranks a distribution system's performance in 52 areas compared with other systems nationwide, in the same state, with the same power supplier, of approximately the same size, and with a similar rate of growth. CFC provides a similar service to G&T cooperatives with its TREND analysis. Differences in an individual system's performance in a certain area from those to which it is compared may not be cause for concern, but it should send management looking for the reason. These analyses can be very helpful in directing management attention to potential problem areas.

PATRONAGE CAPITAL

Patronage capital, capital credits, member equity—by any name, any co-op revenues in excess of expenses, or margins, are investments by the members in the organization and ultimately belong to the members and should be returned to them. Patronage capital is allocated to individual members based on the member's use of electricity, or contribution to margins. A cooperative member does not receive a return on this investment in the cooperative, other than the ability to buy power essentially at cost.

There are several methods for retiring patronage capital, that is, giving it back to the members. The original model bylaws developed by REA provided for retirement of capital credits on a first-in, first-out (FIFO) basis. The **FIFO method** returns oldest investments first, without regard to the level of investment. The period of time the cooperative uses the investment before returning it to the members is called the rotation cycle. For example, suppose a cooperative were rotating patronage capital using the FIFO method and a 20-year rotation cycle. In 1995, the co-op would refund an amount equal to the margins earned in 1975 to the people who were members of the cooperative in 1975 in accordance with their usage of electricity in 1975.

The **percentage method** returns capital in accordance with a percentage of the total amount of capital credits on the cooperative's books and the member's total contribution to the capital credits. For example, in 1994, a typical distribution system had about $15 million in patronage capital on its books and utility operating margins of $1.2 million. If the system decided that it could afford to use $200,000 of the margin to retire patronage capital, it would refund $200,000/$15 million, or 1.3 percent of each member's total allocated patronage capital, accumulated over all the years the member had purchased electricity from the cooperative.

The percentage method is now favored by many cooperatives, because it provides current members with a tangible demonstration of the advantages of cooperative membership. With the changing demographics in many co-op service areas, a member who waits 20 years for a patronage capital refund may well be living in another area and buying power from another electric supplier by the time a refund is received. It may be necessary for a cooperative to amend its bylaws in order to use the percentage method.

Some cooperatives also make special patronage capital retirements. Most common are retirements to the estates of deceased members, but there have also been retirements to members reaching age 65 and to members leaving the cooperative. In today's business climate, these special retirements are generally discouraged by lenders and co-op leaders.

The original REA mortgage required borrowers to achieve a 40 percent equity level in order to retire patronage capital without REA approval. Many in the rural electric program have argued that such a restriction is too severe. The new RUS loan security documents address the issue in the loan agreement, rather than the mortgage. These documents allow borrowers to make general retirements without RUS approval with an equity level of 30 percent and allow special retirements under some circumstances with lower levels of equity. Approximately 91 percent of distribution borrowers had an equity level of 30 percent or more at the time RUS proposed these changes. Therefore, the new loan policies should provide much more latitude for co-ops to develop patronage capital policies that make sense for their individual system.

CHAPTER 10

RURAL UTILITIES SERVICE—
PRIMARY SOURCE OF COOPERATIVE DEBT

RUS, the successor to REA, continues to be the primary source of debt capital for the rural electric program. It provides both direct insured loans and loan guarantees. As noted earlier in Chapter 2, The Rural Electrification Loan Restructuring Act of 1993 (RELRA) mandated a number of changes in traditional loan programs.

RUS continues to be charged with the responsibility for making loans to provide and improve service to rural consumers, and its borrowers are expected to make a diligent effort to serve all consumers in their service area. RELRA defines a rural area as any area not included within the boundaries of an urban area as defined by the Bureau of the Census. It has long been REA policy to determine whether an area is rural at the time an initial loan is made and to allow subsequent loans, even if the nature of the area changes. RELRA also allows RUS to make loans and loan guarantees to improve service to systems in rural areas that were not originally financed by REA.

Prior to the passage of RELRA, REA offered insured electric loans at a standard interest rate of five percent and loans with a rate as low as two percent in cases of extreme financial hardship as determined by the agency administrator. As a result of RELRA, RUS insured electric loans are now offered at a municipal rate or hardship rate of five percent. The agency no longer makes two percent loans. The terms and conditions of loans approved prior to the passage of RELRA are not changed.

RUS LOAN PROGRAMS

Municipal Rate Loans
Municipal rate loans carry an interest rate tied to a published index of municipal rates. Under present policy, the rates are established quarterly, based on the indexes published in *The Bond Buyer*. RUS is authorized to make loans with a maturity of up to 35 years, not to exceed the useful life of the equipment. For the life of the loan, systems may select interest rates for terms of three months up to 35-year final maturity date of the loan. At the end of a term, the co-op can pay the outstanding balance of the loan or roll it over for an additional term.

Cooperatives who serve in areas with either low consumer density (less than 5.5 consumers per mile of line) or a combination of high rate disparity (defined as

THINKING ABOUT FINANCIAL RISK

Until recently, most cooperative distribution systems borrowed a large portion of the funds they needed from REA at an attractive interest rate that was fixed for 35 years. More loan options were available from supplemental lenders. Since the proportion of funds borrowed from supplemental lenders was usually 30 percent or less, the decision on an individual loan had a relatively small impact on overall costs.

Recent changes in the RUS program have given cooperatives greater flexibility in selecting interest rates and loan maturities. They have also exposed cooperatives to market risks that did not exist under the previous program. Most systems will want to manage that risk by balancing debt with shorter and longer term maturities as well as fixed and variable rates. It is important that each system develop a financial management plan that takes into account existing debt and equity levels, TIER and equity goals, cash flows, future financing needs, and market conditions to determine what the best balance is and to establish a systematic approach to interest rate management.

The capital markets offer a number of tools for managing interest rate risk that may be appropriate for cooperatives in certain circumstances. One of the most common is the **interest rate swap**. This requires a minimum debt amount of $10 million in the case of a commercial bank. A cooperative considering a swap should also have an investment-grade rating of its securities. Swaps are generally used to convert one type of debt, such as floating rate debt, into another type of debt, such as fixed rate debt. (Floating rate debt is based on a money market index, such as the London Interbank Offered Rate, or LIBOR.) The parties don't actually swap loans. They just agree to exchange one interest rate payment for another. Usually the party that owes the greater amount makes a net payment to the other swap participant.

The advantages and disadvantages of a swap depend on a system's objectives. A system that exchanges a fixed rate for a floating rate, for example, can benefit from a decline in interest rates but may be increasing its exposure to the risk of inflation. A system that exchanges a floating rate for a fixed rate has obtained a hedge against inflation but will not benefit if interest rates decline.

A system can also protect variable rate debt from market fluctuations by purchasing a special type of swap, an interest rate cap or collar. The interest rate cap imposes a ceiling on the interest rate for a specified period of time. When the market rate is below the cap, the system pays the market rate. When it is above the cap, the system pays the market rate, and the cap provider pays the difference to the co-op. With an interest rate collar, there is a floor as well as a ceiling to the interest rate. As in the cap, when the market rate is above the cap, the system pays the market rate, and the cap provider pays the difference to the co-op. However, if the market rate falls below the floor, the co-op pays the difference to the cap provider.

Both products provide protection against increasing interest rates and some level of benefit from declining interest rates. They can, however, be very expensive to purchase. Collars are usually less expensive than caps.

CFC and CoBank both offer special assistance to systems wishing to evaluate and mitigate interest rate risk.

rates higher than their state's average) and consumer income below the state average may qualify for a 7 percent interest rate cap on their municipal rate loans. This could be a significant benefit if municipal rates surpass 7 percent. In the third quarter of 1995, however, the municipal interest rates ranged from 4.125 percent for terms ending in fiscal year 1996 to 5.750 percent for terms ending in 2016 or later.

In virtually all cases, RUS now requires cooperatives borrowing under the municipal rate program to obtain supplemental financing from another lender for a portion of the project. RUS does not provide a guarantee for the supplemental loan. The proportion of a loan which must be obtained from a supplemental lender is based on the system's Plant Revenue Ratio (PRR) at the time of the loan approval. In general, a cooperative with a PRR of less than 8.00 must obtain 30 percent of the funds for a project from a supplemental lender. CFC and CoBank are the primary sources of supplemental loans.

REA uses the Plant Revenue Ratio to determine which distribution systems are required to obtain supplemental financing.

$$PRR = \frac{\text{Total Utility Plant}}{\text{Operating Revenue and Patronage Capital} - \text{Cost of Power}}$$

In fiscal year 1995, RUS approved 105 municipal rate loans for a total of $536.3 million. At December 31, 1994, RUS had approved a cumulative total of $24 billion in loans to its borrowers, including $9.9 billion at the two percent interest rate, $13.7 billion at the five percent interest rate, and $452.9 million at the municipal rate.

Hardship Loans

In certain cases, the RUS administrator may approve **hardship loans**, which carry an interest rate of five percent. Recipients of hardship loans are not required to obtain supplemental financing. Hardship loans are available to systems whose residential rate exceeds 15 cents per Kwh. Hardship loans are also available to systems that have residential rates exceeding 120 percent of their state average and serve residential consumers whose income is below their state average. Finally, the administrator may approve hardship loans in cases where the system has experienced an extreme hardship because of factors beyond its control, such as extreme weather conditions or loss of substantial loads.

In fiscal year 1995, RUS approved 22 hardship loans for a total of $74.1 million. There is a larger backlog on hardship loans, because more cooperatives than expected have qualified and the program's loan level has dropped to less than $100 million.

Loan Guarantee Program

RUS has the authority to provide loan guarantees for 100 percent of loans made by other lenders for generation, transmission, and distribution purposes. The federal government guarantees the repayment of loans by such lenders for a term of up to 35 years. The interest rate is negotiated by the borrower and the lender. The guarantee is usually used to finance generation and transmission projects. Most distribution systems borrow through RUS's insured loan programs, while G&T cooperatives obtain most of their financing through the guarantee program.

Most RUS guaranteed loans are funded by the Federal Financing Bank (FFB), an agency of the U.S. Treasury. FFB was established in 1973 to coordinate government and government-assisted financing. FFB usually offers the most economical source of funds.

In fiscal year 1995, RUS approved 8 loan guarantees totaling $300 million. At December 31, 1994, RUS had approved a cumulative total of guarantees of $30.9 billion.

Loan Security

Obviously, RUS must determine that it is feasible to make a loan to a particular borrower. That is, the borrower must be able to repay the loan. In addition, RUS must receive adequate security for the loan in the form of a first mortgage lien on the borrower's assets. (In the case of the few borrowers that are unable to provide a first mortgage lien, such as certain public power districts, REA considers other forms of security, such as a pledge of revenues.) In many respects, the RUS mortgage performs the same function for its borrowers that an indenture does for an investor-owned utility.

In July 1995, RUS finalized a new form of mortgage for distribution borrowers. Concurrently, the agency published proposed rules for new loan contracts. Historically, RUS has exercised a significant level of operational control and oversight through the mortgage. The new documents reduce the agency's oversight powers and shift remaining controls from the mortgage to the loan contract.

The original mortgage required a borrower to obtain the advance approval of RUS before issuing any additional secured debt. The process of getting an RUS lien accommodation for the new debt could be very time-consuming. The new mortgage allows borrowers to issue additional secured notes without the approval of RUS or the other mortgagees if the system meets certain criteria.

These changes give systems much more flexibility than they have had in the past. Cooperatives will be able to respond more quickly to member needs in the increasingly competitive environment of today's electric industry. The changes are also a recognition that the cooperatives have come of age. The level of involvement by RUS in borrowers' activities that was required for the untested systems of 1935 is not appropriate for the sophisticated utility cooperatives of 1995.

RUS Note Buyouts

Some co-op systems seeking increased financing flexibility have chosen to "buy out" of their RUS loans. Twenty-nine systems exercised this option in 1987 when offered a one-time opportunity to prepay all REA debt at a discount rate based on the cost of Aa-rated utility bonds. A 1994 law provided a permanent option for systems to prepay their loans to RUS at a discount based on the government's cost of funds at the time of prepayment. While the economic impact of a note buyout should be neutral, a cooperative that prepays in full is no longer subject to RUS's mortgage and loan contract requirements. This can give the co-op flexibility in pursuing activities that would otherwise require RUS approval. For example, a co-op would be freer to pursue large loads or make major purchases. In addition, a greater range of financing options is available in the private market. A co-op system may be able to structure a financing package which better meets a specific need.

On the other hand, a borrower that prepays any portion of its RUS debt is ineligible for direct or insured loans for 10 years and must forgo unadvanced funds on any approved loans. Additionally, the system is not relieved of obligations under its wholesale power contract to an RUS-financed G&T. However, a system could still request and receive an RUS loan guarantee.

One of the strengths of the rural electric program has been the political unity fostered by the shared reliance on RUS. That bond is diminished through legislative changes that let systems shift to other lenders, and some of the program's cohesiveness could be lost. On the other hand, the systems buying out of their RUS debt tend to be stronger systems capable of obtaining debt from other sources without RUS support, which tends to reserve limited RUS loan funds to cooperatives that most need them.

By May 31, 1995, 34 systems had chosen to prepay their RUS loans under the new policy (in addition to the 29 systems that prepaid in 1987). Approximately 20 additional systems were in the process of doing so.

CHAPTER 11

SUPPLEMENTAL FINANCING

By the early 1960s, rural electric leaders were concerned that REA would not be able to provide all of the financing needed for the program's rapidly growing systems. As noted earlier in Chapter 2, co-op leaders initially attempted to establish a rural electric bank similar to the Farm Credit System to provide additional funding for rural electric purposes. However, the legislation to create the bank was defeated by opposition from investor-owned utilities and some segments of the rural electric program itself. In 1967, NRECA established the 26-member Long-Range Study Committee, a group of rural electric leaders representing all geographic areas of the country and all segments of the rural electric program, to formulate specific recommendations for future financing.

Committee deliberations were completely open to the NRECA membership. It reported fully on its activities and held two series of open forums in different parts of the country to hear members' ideas and suggestions and to discuss alternatives. This process set an important precedent for the way in which the rural electric program has subsequently reached consensus on important issues. The committee presented its recommendations to the NRECA annual meeting in March 1969, and the NRECA membership approved the committee's recommendation to establish a cooperative self-help financing organization. That organization, the National Rural Utilities Cooperative Finance Corporation (CFC), was incorporated in April 1969.

CFC

CFC is a not-for-profit cooperative financial institution with assets totaling $7.1 billion on May 31, 1995. It is owned by more than 1,000 member rural electric systems and related organizations and governed by a 22-member board of directors consisting of eleven managers and eleven directors of member systems. It serves as a financial conduit between its members and the private capital markets and offers a variety of loan, investment, member service, and specialized financing programs.

When CFC was formed, the members agreed to invest in CFC by purchasing subordinated subscription certificates. Originally, members had to purchase additional subordinated certificates in connection with loans and guarantees, but that requirement was largely lifted in late 1993. Both the subscription certificates and the loan and guarantee certificates are unsecured, subordinated debt of CFC. That is, the certificates are junior to any other debt CFC incurs. As such, they serve as

CFC's basic equity. At the end of fiscal year 1995, member subordinated certificates provided 42.3 percent of CFC's total capitalization.

CFC obtains debt from the private capital markets through the issuance of collateral trust bonds, medium-term notes, commercial paper, bank bid notes, and other securities. CFC also issues commercial paper and medium-term notes directly to its members and other qualified investors through its **money desk**. CFC's collateral trust bonds are rated Aa3 by Moody's Investors Service, AA by Standard & Poor's Corporation, and AA by Fitch Investors Service. The attractive ratings enable the organization to raise funds in behalf of its member systems at favorable rates.

CFC offers supplemental loans made concurrently with RUS, usually referred to as long-term concurrent loans. These loans enable co-ops to meet the obligation to obtain 30 percent of total loan funds from a lender other than RUS. CFC was the first organization to make supplemental loans and still has the largest commitment of supplemental loan funds to the program. In addition, CFC offers unsecured lines of credit used by co-ops to meet short-term cash needs, intermediate term loans which are usually secured and may be used to provide interim financing of long-term assets or to finance assets with a short life, and 100 percent long-term loans for projects for which RUS funds are not available or for systems that have prepaid their RUS debt. The loan programs are offered at a variety of fixed and variable interest rates.

CFC also guarantees public and private bonds issued by its members. CFC guarantees have been used to help members obtain the benefits of tax-exempt debt and leveraged leases when such alternatives were available.

In recent years, many cooperatives have begun offering non-electric services to improve the quality of life in their service areas and strengthen their ties to members. These services include telecommunications, water and waste water systems, health services, and business development. CFC's associate member program provides line of credit and long-term loans to nonprofit cooperative organizations owned, operated, or controlled by a CFC member to provide such services. Loans to associate members must be guaranteed by the sponsoring member.

In 1987, CFC organized the Rural Telephone Finance Cooperative (RTFC) to meet the special needs of the rural telecommunications industry. Membership in RTFC is open to organizations which provide telephone or telecommunications services and which are active borrowers of or eligible to receive financing from RUS. RTFC is a controlled affiliate of CFC; five of its directors are elected by the membership while six are designated by CFC. CFC is the sole source of funding for RTFC. On May 31, 1995, RTFC had 388 member systems and total assets of $985.4 million.

The National Cooperative Services Corporation (NCSC) was organized in 1981 to provide special financial services that could not be provided directly by CFC because of tax, regulatory, or other concerns. NCSC is a taxable cooperative owned by member rural electric distribution systems. It has an independent board of directors.

CFC provides management services to NCSC through a contractual arrangement. CFC provides direct loans to NCSC and guarantees NCSC debt.

In addition to loans and guarantees, CFC provides a variety of services to its members, including:

- the paying agent service, which allows members to manage their cash by making payments directly from a CFC line of credit or maturing commercial paper to lenders, power suppliers and others.

- specialized rate and regulatory services, including cost of service studies and rate seminars, as well as expert CFC testimony in support of member systems in state regulatory proceedings.

- merger and acquisition studies to evaluate the benefits of potential consolidations.

- financial analysis software.

CFC's Education Fund provides grants to support cooperative education programs. CFC also administers the Cooperative System Integrity Fund, which provides assistance to rural electric systems facing takeover or annexation threats. The fund is supported by voluntary member contributions from CFC patronage capital refunds.

CoBank

CoBank is one of the banks of the Farm Credit System, a nationwide system of cooperatively owned banks and associations first established by Congress in 1916 to provide long-term credit for agricultural purposes. Today, the Farm Credit System, with $66 billion in assets, operates a network of lending institutions that provide production agriculture with one-quarter of its credit needs.

The Farm Credit System also includes one Bank for Cooperatives (BC) and seven Federal Credit Banks. The Federal Credit Banks serve various Federal Land Bank Associations, Production Credit Associations, Agriculture Credit Associations, and Federal Land Credit Associations. CoBank and the Farm Credit Banks supervise the activities of the associations they serve, which make loans for the benefit of their borrowers for qualified agricultural purposes.

The Farm Credit Act of 1933 expanded the role of the Farm Credit Systems by creating 13 BCs, including 12 district BCs and a large Central Bank for Cooperatives to serve large accounts and those crossing district lines. The Farm Credit Act of 1971, which generally governs the operations of the Farm Credit System today, authorized the BCs to finance rural electric and telephone cooperatives. In 1989, 11 of the BCs consolidated to form CoBank—National Bank for Cooperatives. In 1995, CoBank, the Springfield Bank for Cooperatives, and the Farm Credit Bank of Springfield consolidated to form CoBank, ACB. That event was the first consolidation of a Farm Credit Bank with a Bank for Cooperatives. The new organization has $16 billion in assets, $13 billion in loans outstanding, and $1 billion in capital.

While the government provided seed money for the initial capitalization of the BCs and other Farm Credit Banks, those funds were repaid in 1968. CoBank is now owned by approximately 2,300 stockholders, including U.S. agricultural cooperatives, rural utility systems, Farm Credit associations, and other businesses providing rural services. About 2,000 of the stockholders are also customers of the bank.

CoBank is governed by a 39-member board of directors, 38 of whom are elected by the stockholders. One member is appointed by the board. The bank operates on a cooperative basis. Historically, a substantial portion of the bank's earnings has been returned to its customers in the form of patronage capital refunds. Additional funds for CoBank lending programs are obtained primarily from the sale of Farm Credit System securities.

About 400 of CoBank's 2,000 customers are rural utility systems, including 30 G&T systems and 160 distribution and related customers. The bank has loans and commitments to rural utilities of $3.3 billion, including $2.3 billion to G&Ts and $719 million to distribution systems. CoBank may serve any system eligible to borrow from RUS or the Rural Telephone Bank. Other utilities may be able to borrow from the bank if farmers control at least 60 percent of the organization. In addition, CoBank finances joint ventures involving ownership by eligible customers and subsidiaries of eligible customers. It can also participate in loans involving customers that are not eligible to borrow directly from the bank if the customer derives a majority of its income from or a majority of its assets are invested in utilities. In 1990, CoBank was authorized to finance water and waste disposal systems for unincorporated areas or communities of less than 20,000 people.

CoBank offers a variety of lending services to meet its borrowers' needs, including construction loans, operating loans, interim financing for systems awaiting RUS loans, and long-term loans and lines of credit. It has also funded RUS buy-outs for a number of systems. A range of interest rate alternatives, including fixed and variable rates, is available. The bank makes concurrent supplemental term loans with RUS and provides funds under the RUS guaranteed loan program for refinancing of FFB loans. It provides leasing services through the Farm Credit Leasing Services Corp. CoBank also syndicates and participates in utility and telecommunications loans and acts as agent or co-agent on syndications.

Other financial services offered include interest rate risk management products, back-up lines of credit to assist customers in selling commercial paper or other debt instruments, cash investment services, and letters of credit.

In addition to its activities with rural utilities and other rural businesses, CoBank is authorized to finance agricultural exports and provide international banking services for the benefit of U.S. farmer-owned cooperatives and American agriculture.

Other Sources of Financing

While RUS, CFC, and CoBank have provided most of the debt capital for the rural electric program, there are other sources of funding. Cooperative Utilities Finance Corporation, an organization patterned after CFC, provides financing for 11 member systems located in New Mexico. Some cooperative organizations, such as G&Ts, have offered special financing services to their member systems. And a few cooperatives have established their own indentures and borrowed directly from the private capital markets.

CHAPTER 12

BORROWING FROM THE PRIVATE CAPITAL MARKETS

Historically, the rural electric program has obtained most of its financing from government sources. Additional financing is available, however, from the many individuals and organizations investing in the business activities of other organizations through the operations of the private capital market. The government, CFC, CoBank, and a few cooperatives obtain their funding directly from these sources. Private investments take a number of forms, and the cost to the business receiving the investment depends on the amount of financial risk the investors associate with the company and the investment instrument as well as financial market conditions. Of course, many companies are competing for this capital. The greater an organization's financial strength, the lower the risk investors attribute to it.

Bonds—Debt Securities

A bond is a debt security, essentially a loan from an investor that must be repaid, while stock is an equity security, a purchase of ownership in an organization. The bond itself may be called a bond certificate or indenture. It is evidence of the ownership of the bond, and of the amount, or denomination. There are three commonly used types of bonds:

- **mortgage bonds**, secured by a mortgage on the land, buildings, and other physical property of the utility

- **debenture bonds**, secured by the general credit of the company, but subordinate to the senior claim of all mortgage bonds

- **revenue bonds**, secured by the ability of the issuing company to earn enough net revenue over and above senior claims to pay interest and eventually to repay the principal amount

Each type of bond offers a different degree of risk. Mortgage bonds are considered the safest, because if the debt is not paid according to the terms of the bonds, foreclosure proceedings can be brought against the property—just like a home mortgage. Debenture bonds are next. If they are not paid according to the terms of the bond, the bondholders may get a court judgment on the default, just like any other unpaid creditor. They may also have receivers appointed to take over the company's affairs, subject to any senior claims of outstanding mortgage bonds. Revenue bonds have the greatest risk, because they can only be paid if sufficient revenues are earned. All debt instruments, including bonds, are paid ahead of stockholders, in the case of privately-owned companies, and members, in the case of electric cooperatives.

There may also be differences as to the time when bonds are redeemed. Mortgage bonds, for example, may be issued as first mortgage bonds, second mortgage bonds (rarely used by utilities), and so forth. First mortgage bonds have priority over second mortgage bonds. There may also be some differences in maturity, that is, the final date on which the principal must be repaid.

The bonds may be issued serially; that is, the bonds of one series may have a different maturity date than another series. By spreading out maturity dates over a period of years, it may be easier for the company to repay the principal amounts than if they all fell due at the same time. Bonds may also be called, or paid ahead of their maturity date, if the bond contains a call provision. Sometimes the bond specifies a premium, a bonus, which must be paid to the bondholder if the bond is called before the maturity date. A noncallable bond, which is favored by large institutional investors, must be allowed to run to maturity. When interest rates on debt declined in the late 1980s, many companies examined their ability to call some of their high-interest bonds. If the savings from a lower interest rate was greater than the call premium, refinancing the debt made sense.

Mortgage bonds may be closed end or open end bonds. Closed end bonds require that any additional borrowing must be done by a new series with a new mortgage. Open end bonds permit the company to issue additional bonds as the company acquires additional property, which is pledged as security. Most utility bond issues in recent years have been open end.

Some bond indentures include a **sinking-fund** provision. This requires the company to set aside money to repay the principal, over and above the interest payments on the bonds and before any dividends can be paid out on stock. This makes the repayment at maturity more secure. Since the interest rates on bonds reflect the level of risk perceived by the investor, a sinking fund provision would lower the interest rate on a bond.

Sometimes a company may pay off one series of bonds with the proceeds from another issue, called a refunding issue.

Tax-Exempt Bond Financing

Prior to the Tax Reform Act of 1986, cooperatives and other organizations could issue tax-exempt bonds to finance pollution control facilities and certain facilities related to industrial development. Since the bondholder does not have to pay state or federal income taxes on the interest earnings, tax-exempt bonds had a lower rate than funds borrowed under the REA guarantee program. In the late 1970s and early 1980s, as much as 30 percent of the cost of a generating project was for pollution control facilities, so many G&Ts took advantage of the opportunity of reducing costs through tax-exempt financing. The Tax Reform Act of 1986 eliminated most new opportunities for this form of financing, but many systems still have tax-exempt debt outstanding.

Leveraged Leases

Another type of tax-advantaged financing that was attractive prior to the Tax Reform Act of 1986 was the **leveraged lease**. While leveraged leases are quite complex, the concept is simple. In essence, a company that does not have a high income tax liability sells a facility to a company that does have a high income tax liability. The purchaser, or lessor, invests a limited amount of equity in the project and borrows the rest of the cost from a third party lender through a loan secured by a mortgage on the facility and a pledge of the lease rentals. Since the lessor has no need for the actual asset, it leases the facility back to the seller, or lessee. The lessor is, however, entitled to the tax benefits of ownership and shares those benefits with the lessee through the lease payments, which are lower than the lessee's cost of ownership would have been.

Cooperatives have participated in more than $1 billion of leveraged leases. The Tax Reform Act of 1986 eliminated most of the tax benefits that made leveraged leases attractive.

Commercial Paper

Commercial paper is a form of short-term unsecured debt that has a specific maturity, usually from one to 270 days. It is represented by a promissory note, or contract between borrower and lender. It carries a money market interest rate and can be an attractive source for short-term investments. Commercial paper is normally sold through an agent, such as an investment bank. The expense of issuing commercial paper is such that it is not attractive to small borrowers. However, many cooperatives routinely invest in commercial paper through CFC and CoBank as a part of their cash management activities.

Medium-Term Notes

Medium-term notes are unsecured obligations with a longer term to maturity than commercial paper ranging from 271 days up to 30 years.

Ratings

The ratings assigned by independent rating agencies are an assessment of the borrower's ability to repay principal and interest. Each of an organization's different financial instruments, such as collateral trust bonds, commercial paper, and guarantees, receives a separate rating. The best known of the investor service companies, or rating agencies, are Moodys Investors Service, Standard & Poor's Corporation, Fitch Investors Service, and Duff and Phelps.

The rating agencies study a company and its financial position and rate its securities as to quality. Each company has established a range of possible ratings which reflect the relative investment quality of the security. The ratings, in effect, constitute a measure of the degree of risk involved. The securities with the least risk are given the highest rating.

FIGURE 12.1. Bond Ratings and Definitions

Duff & Phelps¹	Fitch¹	Moody's²	S&P¹	Definition
AAA	AAA	Aaa	AAA	High-grade investment bonds. The highest rating assigned, denoting extremely strong capacity to pay principal and interest. Often called "gilt edge" securities.
AA	AA	Aa	AA	High-grade investment bonds. High quality by all standards, but rate lower primarily because the margins of protection are not quite as strong.
A	A	A	A	Medium-grade investment bonds. Many favorable investment attributes, but elements may be present which suggest susceptibility to adverse economic changes.
BBB	BBB	Baa	BBB	Medium-grade investment bonds. Adequate capacity to pay principal and interest but possibly lacking certain protective elements against adverse economic conditions.
BB	BB	Ba	BB	Speculative issues. Only moderate protection of principal and interest in varied economic times.
B	B	B	B	Speculative issues. Generally lacking desirable characteristics of investment bonds. Assurance of principal and interest may be small.
CCC	CCC	Caa	CCC	Default. Poor-quality issue that may be in default or in danger of default.
	CC	Ca	CC	Default. Highly speculative issues, often in default or possessing other marked shortcomings.
		C		Default. These issues may be regarded as extremely poor in investment quality.
	C		C	Default. Rating given to income bonds on which no interest is paid.
	D		D	Default. Issues actually in default, with principal or interest in arrears.

¹*Duff & Phelps, Fitch, Standard and Poor's use plus (+) and minus (−) which correspond to Moody's 1 and 3 modifiers.*

²*Beginning April 26, 1982, Moody's began applying the numerical modifiers 1, 2 and 3 in each generic rating classification from Aa through B in its corporate bond rating system. The modifier 1 indicates that the security ranks in the higher end of its generic rating category; the modifier 2 indicates a mid-range ranking; and the modifier 3 indicates that the issue ranks in the lower end of its generic rating category.*

SOURCE: *Duff & Phelps Inc. Credit Decisions, Fitch Rating Register, Moody's Bond Record and Standard and Poor's Bond Guide.*

For such a service to be of value, the ratings must be carefully made under uniform standards of evaluation. The rating agencies make a detailed study of past financial history, quality of management, revenues and their stability, the sources of the company's business, contractual relations with other companies, capital structure, and so forth. The ratings may be changed from time to time as individual company circumstances change.

Generally speaking, bonds which carry a rating of BBB or higher are considered investment grade bonds. Investments in bonds which carry a rating of BB or lower are considered more speculative. Many institutional and government investors have criteria which do not allow them to invest in bonds below a certain grade.

In general, the higher the rating of the bond, the better the price at which it can be sold and the lower the interest which has to be paid. Thus, a company with the highest rating may gain two ways: more money will be available when it sells bonds, and it will pay less interest over the life of the bond.

In most instances, the most attractive form of financing available to cooperatives is through the RUS, CFC, or CoBank lending programs. From time to time, however, there are circumstances when a cooperative may find it advantageous to issue bonds. The credit rating of the bond issue can be enhanced through the use of a guarantee by a third party that agrees to repay the debt in the event of a default by the cooperative. In that case, the rating agency looks to the credit strength of the guarantor in assigning a rating. CFC has provided guarantees for its members for tax-exempt debt, lease transactions, and other financings.

How Bonds are Sold

A cooperative that chooses to borrow from an organization such as CFC is spared the effort and expense of issuing bonds on its own. For a small system that may not qualify for a high rating, the expense of going it alone may be prohibitive. Almost a dozen G&T and distribution systems have obtained independent ratings in order to issue their own securities. Others may well do so in the future.

There are two general ways in which new securities, such as bonds, are sold: public sales and private sales. A public sale is an offering of a new security to the general public. A private sale, or private placement, is the sale of a security to an individual, another company, or to institutional investors without a public offering. Private placements have been increasing in recent years. The major institutional buyers are insurance companies, endowment funds, trust funds, mutual investment funds, universities, labor unions, and even foreign investment interests.

Bond offerings are made through investment bankers. Investment banking firms are specialists in selling securities and provide many services to the company wishing to sell its bonds. The most important service is to act as underwriter for the bonds. The underwriter purchases the bond issue for sale to other investors. In other words, an underwriter guarantees that the bonds will be sold. A group of investment bankers known as a syndicate often agree to underwrite the bonds together.

There are several methods for selling bonds. The sale frequently requires competitive bidding, which involves notice to the public. The first public announcement of proposed bond issue, inviting sealed bids, is likely to be in the form of an advertisement in the financial section of local and financial newspapers. This advertisement generally gives information about the amount of the issue and where further details concerning it and the company may be obtained. The advertisement will also specify the place, date, and time for the opening of the bids.

The advertisement is the culmination of a demanding series of tasks, which require the combined efforts of the company's lawyers, accountants, engineers, financial experts, and others to complete. An organization that wishes to use bond financing must generally comply with the following procedure. If a cooperative requests a guarantee for a bond issue, the guarantor will provide assistance in completing these steps.

- The chief financial officer estimates the amount of capital needed and the form of security to be issued. A co-op must also decide whether to request a loan guarantee. If so, the guarantor should be involved in the process from the early stages.

- Other company officials review the estimates and make any necessary changes. Management makes a recommendation to the board of directors. At this point, the organization should also obtain an opinion of counsel that the proposed issue will qualify under various state laws as legal investment for trust funds or for clearance under special state laws.

- The board of directors authorizes the issue, and management begins preliminary preparation for the regulatory filings.

- The organization files the necessary documents for clearing the issue with regulatory authorities. If the bonds will be sold in interstate commerce, they must meet the requirements of registration with full disclosure of information to the Securities and Exchange Commission. The approval of a state regulatory agency may be required.

- The company must finalize security arrangements. A cooperative may be required to obtain a lien accommodation under the RUS mortgage or other applicable mortgage.

- The rating agencies provide a rating of the security. Although this step is actually not required, it is highly desirable because a recognized rating helps to sell the security.

- The preliminary prospectus, also known as the red herring after the custom of printing it in red ink, is prepared. The preliminary prospectus announces the fact of the pending registration, but points out that it is not yet effective and is still subject to change. It is used mainly to inform prospective underwriters about the proposed security and contains essentially the same information as is found in the registration statement.

- The bidding papers are prepared and issued. These are invitations to prospective purchasers (underwriters) to bid on the bond issue which also give authority to the prospective purchaser to examine any outstanding mortgages or deeds of trust. The bidding papers include the registration statement, the mortgage, the red herring prospectus, the terms under which the bids will be accepted or rejected, and a bidding form upon which the bid is to be submitted. Forms for syndicate or selling agreements to be used by the successful bidder are also commonly included. The market has now moved to a book-entry system of recording the selling and ownership of bonds. The issuing company also makes arrangements for recording the purchase and ownership of the bonds.

- Management and staff meet with the underwriters. The meeting with prospective underwriters is called the due diligence meeting because the Securities Act of 1933 requires that due diligence be exercised by underwriters to inform themselves about the company and the proposed security issue. The meeting is an informal one primarily designed to make further information available. Prospective underwriters are encouraged to ask questions of company officials who are expected to answer openly and fully. Prospective underwriters are likely to ask pointed questions on such matters as regulatory environment, competition, labor conditions, and other issues.

- Bids are opened at the designated time and place. A representative of each bidding group is present to drop a sealed bid in the box provided and to report promptly on the outcome. The form of bid sets forth the interest coupon, the rate of actual yield, and the price offered for the bonds. Each bidding underwriter also has enclosed a check for a small percentage of the principal amount of the bonds to be purchased as evidence of good faith. The checks are returned to unsuccessful bidders.

Company officials open the bids, which can be quickly calculated and tabulated. Within a short time the company is able to announce the acceptance of the best bid, the one resulting in the lowest cost to the company.

After a bid is accepted, the company must sign formal contracts with the underwriter. The board of directors formally approves the transaction. The bonds are then offered for sale to the public by the underwriters through an offering prospectus that is essentially the same as the red herring. Closing usually takes place within a week.

The process of making a securities issue requires a great deal of effort and normally takes at least a month to complete.

WHEN THINGS GO WRONG

In recent years, a few cooperative systems experiencing extreme financial difficulties have been forced to default on debt service payments to REA and other lenders. The most common cause was a commitment to generation resources planned to meet demands that did not materialize. In other cases, the system built a plant that was needed but that had a cost substantially higher than that available from other resources. In another case, the partner of a participant in a joint participation project unilaterally scrapped the project, leaving the cooperative with large loans and no plant. These situations resulted in stranded costs, or investments that the co-op could not recover in a reasonable of time. In another case, the board of directors failed to establish appropriate rate and financial policies.

Distribution systems, of course, can be affected by the financial difficulties of their G&T. In difficult situations there is often a basic conflict between the interests of the G&T in establishing wholesale rates sufficient to cover its costs and the member distribution systems that must have low enough retail rates to compete with other suppliers. Problems can develop because the people responsible for solving the G&T's problems, its board of directors, are elected by member distribution systems that may be asked to pay higher rates as a result.

Some systems experiencing financial difficulties have been able to negotiate with REA and other lenders to restructure their debt. At the end of fiscal year 1993, REA reported that it had negotiated restructuring agreements for debt totaling more than $8 billion with 10 borrowers. The agency was continuing negotiations with and oversight on seven other financially troubled borrowers with outstanding debt to the federal government of $5.7 billion. Four electric borrowers were in default and had not entered into restructuring agreements with the government.

Some systems that were unable or chose not to negotiate a restructuring of their debt have filed for voluntary reorganization under Chapter 11 of the U.S. Bankruptcy Code. This action does not offer a simple solution to the problem of financial insolvency. Wabash Valley Power Association, an Indiana G&T, filed for bankruptcy protection on May 23, 1985. The Bankruptcy Court confirmed the cooperative's reorganization plan—which included a significant reduction in its RUS debt—pending rate approvals on August 7, 1991. The U.S. District Court affirmed the plan on June 22, 1994. RUS appealed the decision to the U.S. Court of Appeals. At this writing, the Appeals Court had not issued a decision. During much of the time this was occurring neither Wabash nor its member systems were able to obtain additional financing because of lenders' concerns about loan security, the regulatory climate in Indiana, and member obligations under the wholesale power contract. In addition, other Indiana cooperatives uninvolved in the Wabash situation were unable to obtain financing for part of that time period because of RUS concerns about the regulatory situation in Indiana.

In another example, Colorado-Ute Electric Association, a Colorado G&T, filed a voluntary petition for bankruptcy protection on March 30, 1990. A reorganization plan filed on September 26, 1991, allowed all creditors to recover their loans to Colorado-Ute. The cooperative itself, however, was liquidated, and its assets were sold to other utilities, including another Colorado-based G&T. The relatively quick disposition was attributed to the appointment of an independent trustee and to the fact that the cooperative's assets were basically sound.

Speaking at CFC's 1991 Power Supply Symposium, Victor Palmieri, the trustee, attributed Colorado-Ute's problems to the co-op's inability to make changes to deal with the collapse of the economy in western Colorado in the 1980s, excess generating capacity, and poor management practices, in particular a weak board which typically deferred to strong managers.

He outlined several alternatives financially troubled cooperatives can consider to resolve a cash flow crisis, including:

• increasing revenue by raising rates

• decreasing expenses by cutting costs

• renegotiating high-cost fuel contracts

• negotiating with creditors to reschedule or restructure debt service

• selling assets

• merging with another utility

Essentially, anything that can be accomplished through bankruptcy can be accomplished through other means. However, management and board members sometimes find it hard to make difficult decisions about selling assets or merging. It is important to remember that the management and the board of directors have a fiduciary responsibility to the cooperative, it lenders, and its members. In certain circumstances they may be held personally liable for any losses. In addition, these events do not occur in a vacuum. The ratings of several G&T systems and CFC were downgraded specifically as a result of other systems' financial difficulties.

CHAPTER 13

TAX ISSUES

A common myth voiced by many is that electric cooperatives do not pay taxes. Cooperatives pay the taxes that other businesses pay and some that apply only to utilities. Depending on state and local tax laws, the following types of taxes may apply.

Property taxes are based on the value of real estate, personal property, or intangible property. Such taxes are usually imposed at the local level and are a mainstay of local government.

Revenue taxes may be imposed on gross receipts or otherwise be based on revenue. They may take the place of or be in addition to property taxes.

Franchise taxes are a local form of taxation usually imposed by a city or town on the utility for the privilege of provide service within city limits. It may be based on property values, gross receipts, or other measures.

Occupational taxes are also imposed in return for the privilege of doing business locally, but not necessarily on an exclusive basis. They can be levied on all types of businesses, not just utilities.

Excise taxes are imposed on the manufacture, sale, or consumption of commodities and services, such as the tax on telephone service or interstate passenger fares.

Social Security taxes must be paid by all forms of business, including cooperatives, based on payrolls, to provide for unemployment insurance, pensions, and other benefits provided under the Social Security Act. Cooperatives withhold a part of employees' wages and salaries in contribution to these social benefits, just as all other business employers do.

Energy export taxes exist in various forms as taxes imposed by the states on the production, transmission, or distribution of natural resources and derivative forms of energy, such as generated electricity. Examples include a severance tax on the mining of coal or a tax on the commercial development of natural gas taken from state lands. States defend the taxes on the ground that states must be compensated for the social and environmental effects of energy production activities.

Many cooperatives do not, however, pay income taxes. Most cooperatives do not earn income, having a legal obligation to return any margins to their members. Since they have no income, they are generally exempt from paying state and federal income tax if 85 percent or more of their revenue comes from members. Some cooperative systems have elected to become subject to federal income taxes through participation in tax-advantaged financing opportunities, like leveraged leases.

The taxes paid by a cooperative are a part of its operating expenses.

PROPERTY VALUATION

From time to time, a cooperative needs to know the value of its investments in facilities. **Valuation** is the process of determining that dollar amount. The cooperative's property taxes depend on the valuation, and it can also be a factor in mergers or sales of service territory.

There are several basic methods of property valuation. The **original cost** method is based on the cost of procuring the property, including the money actually spent to purchase the property and the cost of any additions and improvements. When a property is acquired after it has been built or operated by one or more previous owners, including another utility, original cost may mean the cost of acquisition at the time that the property was first taken over by a utility and put into service for the benefit of utility customers. The cost figures, or book cost, should be available in the books and records of the former owner.

The **reproduction cost** method is based on the cost of reproducing the property at the time the valuation is made. A complete valuation of this nature involves an appraisal of the property in terms of current prices and attempts to quantify what it would cost to construct or acquire the property today, regardless of when it was originally built or acquired.

The **market value** method is based on a market test. For example, the stock of an investor-owned utility is traded every day, and investors thus place a value on what they will pay for the stock. Since cooperatives do not have stockholders, this method is usually not available to them.

Most co-op valuations are based on the **income method**, which calculates the value of the property based on the income it generates. One of the major difficulties in using this method for cooperatives is determining the appropriate rate of return, or capitalization rate. A cooperative tries to produce the lowest possible rates for its members rather than to maximize income. Therefore, co-ops tend to use a rate of return that would be appropriate to an investor-owned utility for valuation purposes.

As an example, if a cooperative received a net margin of $1 million on a property and used a 10 percent rate of return, the value of the property would be $1 million/.10, or $10 million.

FINANCING COOPERATIVES IN THE FUTURE

Electric cooperatives, like other electric utilities, are capital intensive organizations. The loan and guarantee programs and other support provided by REA and its successor RUS have made it possible for cooperatives to obtain the financing required to build and operate all types of facilities needed to serve their members.

Because of the REA program, cooperatives today are strong, fiscally sound organizations. They have created their own cooperative financing organization, CFC, to provide additional access to capital. Some have also developed a relationship with CoBank, a traditional source of funding for agriculture-related cooperatives. A few have even been successful in working with the investment community at large.

Cooperatives face the same challenges others face in the evolving competitive environment of the electric industry. They do so with a history of a strong system of financial support.

PART

REGULATION AND RATES

CHAPTER 14

RATES AND REGULATORY ISSUES

Every state in the union has a public service commission or some similar body to oversee the provision and pricing of essential services like natural gas and electricity, telecommunications, and passenger and freight transportation. These state regulatory bodies have broad review and approval powers over the operations of investor-owned electric utilities, but their authority over electric cooperatives varies a great deal from state to state.

The extent of state regulation which co-ops face ranges from none at all—commissions in nine states have no jurisdiction over co-ops—to full control of retail rates. In 25 of the 46 states where co-ops provide power, however, they are not subject to rate regulation because of their nonprofit structure and the ability of member-owners to elect directors.

Regulation of public services dates to long before the formation of electric utilities. In the late 17th Century, England's Chief Justice Matthew Hale declared that certain kinds of business were "affected with a public interest." English courts held that privately owned ferries, highways, toll bridges, and stagecoach lines served an overriding public interest, and thus could be required to provide universal service at reasonable cost.

This concept became the basis for U.S. regulation of vital public services. In 1820, Congress gave the city of Washington regulatory powers over bread prices, chimney sweeps and wharves. Rhode Island and other New England states followed in the mid-1800s with the formation of advisory commissions to oversee rail service.

State regulatory powers expanded in the late 1800s under the influence of the Grange, a prairie-state agricultural movement. Monopolistic abuses by railroad companies led farmers to demand laws regulating the prices rail lines could charge for transporting their grain, and state authority over rail charges was upheld by the Supreme Court in 1877. Georgia, New York, and Wisconsin established the first of the modern public service commissions in 1907, and by 1920 most states had followed suit.

In the 1990s, however, many commissions have begun re-examining their roles. The emergence of strongly competitive wholesale power markets, pressures for greater competition at the retail level and a general trend toward less government regulation have begun to modify their authority over what were once viewed as a natural monopolies.

Wisconsin's Public Service Commission, for example, conducted a series of public hearings in late 1995 on its detailed study of the likely outcomes of electric utility deregulation in that state. The commission study concluded that short-term rate decreases would probably yield to long-term increases as investment risks in an unstable, competitive market drove financing costs up. Consumers would probably enjoy more price and service options, the Wisconsin study added, but it also warned that "unchecked market power...could cause significant upward pressure on prices."

The regulatory agency in most states is known as the public service commission or public utilities commission. Other names include commerce or corporation commission, board of utility control and utility regulatory commission. Whatever the regulatory body's formal title, its duties combine three functions—legislative, judicial, and administrative—normally assigned to separate branches of the government.

The commission's legislative authority rests in its power to make rules to carry out utility laws. It acts in a judicial capacity by conducting legal hearings—often using officials called administrative law judges—in rate or service hearings. Its administrative powers come into play when it enforces its orders and rulings. This consolidation of power gives commissions greater flexibility in regulating vital public services.

Commission rulings are final and binding in all states; they cannot be revised or overruled by another branch of government. However, when consumers or utilities question the commission's power or a legislative action changing the commission's authority, the dispute may be resolved in court.

Most state commissions consist of three or five members, although Illinois and the Carolinas have seven-member regulatory agencies. The constitutions of nine states call for regulatory commissions; the rest were created by legislatures. Voters in 13 states elect commissioners, but the more common approach is gubernatorial appointment and Senate confirmation.

STATE REGULATION OF ELECTRIC COOPERATIVES

Utility regulation represents a compromise between the free-market principle of competition regulating supply and demand and the economic pressures that result in natural monopolies providing essential basic services. By establishing service requirements and ruling on whether rates are "just and reasonable," regulators serve as a substitute for competition to balance the utility investor's demand for profits against the consumer's demand for adequate, reasonably priced service.

This basic conflict of interests between owners and consumers, however, does not exist for cooperatives, where consumers and owners are one and the same. Cooperatives do not have a profit motivation. Their purpose is to provide adequate power to consumer-members at reasonable prices. Cooperative consumers have the opportunity to exercise control over the operation of their utility through their power to elect directors. For these reasons, co-op consumers do not require the additional protection of outside regulators.

Nevertheless, the 1995 survey of state commissions by the National Association of Regulatory Utility Commissioners revealed that regulators in 21 states have "authority to regulate or control" co-op retail rates. Florida's Public Service Commission has authority over rate structure, while state rate regulation is optional for co-ops in Iowa, Kansas, and Minnesota.

Streamlined or expedited rate regulation in eight states allows co-ops to adopt changes within certain specified ranges without lengthy hearings and approvals, according to a 1994 survey by NRECA. In Oklahoma, for example, co-ops do not need to file a rate case if the increase is less than three percent of the system's annual revenue; in Maine, increases of fifteen percent or less can be adopted without commission approval unless 750 members, or ten percent of the membership, object.

System financing may also come under commission review. The 1994 NRECA survey found that co-ops in five states must get regulatory approval of short-term financing and an additional 14 states regulate co-op financial commitments of one year or more.

Rate regulation carries a bottom-line cost for cooperative electric utilities. Composite TIER and equity levels of co-ops in regulated states are much lower than those of unregulated co-ops, reflecting regulatory preferences for lower consumer rates over higher margins and other financial goals. In addition, regulatory rate cases can prove expensive.

But state commissions are hardly the only regulatory bodies that concern co-ops. Numerous federal agencies keep track of co-op financial, environmental and energy-policy performance. At the top of the list for the vast majority of co-ops is RUS.

RUS AS REGULATOR

The Rural Electrification Act of 1936 made the Rural Electrification Administration and its successor agency, the Rural Utilities Service, responsible for bringing universal electric service to the nation's rural areas and for protecting the security on government loans provided to utility systems that agreed to carry out that purpose. Since the government's loan security took the form of a mortgage on all assets of its borrowers, REA had a strong interest in seeing that the system remained financially and operationally viable.

REA's dual role of electrifying the countryside and safeguarding the federal investment provided the basis for its wide-ranging oversight of co-op activities. Electric co-ops were required to get the agency's approval on rate structures and levels, financial and engineering plans, manager appointments, and even expenditures of more than $25,000 for land or equipment. The agency established system design and construction standards and maintained a list of materials approved for use by borrowers.

Other federal regulatory agencies, such as the Federal Power Commission and its successor, the Federal Energy Regulatory Commission, generally deferred to REA in recognition of both its authority and its expertise in setting operating, financial, and service standards. State commissions have occasionally attempted to override REA requirements, usually after the agency demanded higher rates to ensure loan repayments. The federal government almost always responds to those efforts by taking the matter to state or federal court.

Most judges accept the RUS argument that the federal purpose of electrifying the country, stated and maintained by Congress in the Rural Electrification Act, preempts state actions under the supremacy clause of the U.S. Constitution. Federal lawyers have not won every case, however. One notable exception is the decade-long bankruptcy battle involving Wabash Valley Power Association, an Indiana generation and transmission cooperative. (For a more detailed discussion of this case, see Chapter 6). The Indiana Utility Regulatory Commission refused to approve rate increases REA said the G&T needed to cover repayment of loans on a failed nuclear project. The commission argued that consumers should not have to pay for a project that was not "used and useful." State and federal judges agreed with state regulators that the federal government's mortgages and loan agreements failed to spell out its ratesetting power, and the case remained unresolved at the end of 1995.

For more than half a century, electric co-op managers and directors accepted REA oversight in exchange for the benefits of REA financing. But a combination of factors surfacing in the late 1980s and early 1990s caused some systems to reconsider this relationship.

For one thing, the growing federal budget deficit and political pressures to reduce it chipped away at REA loan levels. The agency's "first come, first served" policy in approving new loans produced long delays in receiving vital financing for expanding and upgrading co-op services. Backlogged direct loan applications totaled more than $700 million at the end of fiscal 1991, and REA entered fiscal 1992 with authority to make $622 million in such loans. As a result, co-ops could expect to wait more than a year to receive loan approvals. Meanwhile, reduced staffing levels at the agency were also resulting in long delays in getting needed approvals for borrowers' plans and projects.

Growing cooperative utilities, faced with increasing competitive pressures from annexing municipal systems and investor-owned companies eager to buy out co-op consumers, could ill afford these financing and approval delays.

Furthermore, the co-ops themselves had changed. Systems that had relied on REA for engineering and technical advice 30 years earlier now had engineers and other experts on staff. Even financing, the mainstay of the agency's service, was increasingly available from other, nongovernment sources. And such outside financing, at least in the eyes of many co-op managers, came without as many strings attached.

Borrower frustrations with financing delays and the need to get approval for routine business operations led NRECA's board to create the Cooperative Finance Study Committee in late 1990. The panel spent 1991 gathering comments and recommendations from the government and its borrowers, and offered a package of suggested improvements in 1992. Many of those suggestions were aimed at reducing what became known, unofficially but universally, as the "hassle factor"—the need to get REA approval for large power-sale agreements, design changes, use of materials not on the agency's list and even sales of buildings and line trucks, as well as the long wait for agency action on such requests.

The NRECA committee's recommendations, as well as a package of other findings by a sister study panel established by CFC, triggered a long process of reviews and proposals at RUS. By the end of 1995, the agency had finalized or proposed changes to its financing documents that reduced the scope of its control over borrower operations and eased restrictions on outside financing.

Meanwhile, more and more co-ops left the government loan program altogether. As early as 1941, co-ops began paying off their REA mortgages; others used discounted prepayments approved by Congress in the late 1980s and early 1990s to buy out of the program. By the end of 1994, a total of 134 borrowers had repaid their REA loans in full.

Forgoing government financing also released co-ops from another "hassle factor" that came with use of federal funds: the need to complete environmental impact statements on any project or activity that used government money. These detailed—and usually costly and time consuming—environmental assessments were not technically an RUS requirement. Under environmental legislation going back to the early 1970s, they apply to any project funded in any way by the government, or requiring government action, and thus extend to co-ops that borrow from RUS. Regardless of their borrowing status, however, co-ops must comply with the same environmental regulations on toxic or hazardous materials and emissions that other govern other companies.

But the upshot is that, by the mid-1990s, electric cooperatives face fewer federal regulatory controls. The extent to which they are subject to state regulators remains highly variable from state to state. Operation of the electric co-op—including the most basic task, that of setting rates—remains, first and finally, the responsibility of the cooperative's member-elected board of directors.

ESTABLISHING CO-OP RATES

A cooperative's nonprofit, member-owned business structure may eliminate the tug-of-war between profits and price that marks investor-owned operations, but it does not free co-op directors from conflict.

Directors themselves buy power for their homes and businesses from the system they oversee, and they are also elected by friends and family members. When they approve rate increases, they are raising the cost of living for themselves and their neighbors. The same pressures apply in the boardrooms of generation and transmission co-ops. G&T directors represent member systems whose biggest cost by far is that of purchased power.

But co-op directors have a fiduciary duty to set aside such personal and parochial concerns to ensure the financial health of their electric cooperatives. The board has a basic responsibility to establish reasonable rates for its members regardless of whether the rates are subject to regulatory review or approval. The rates must be high enough to cover the cooperative's costs and maintain its financial health, but they must also be fair and equitable to the members. In today's competitive climate, rates must also be low enough to attract and retain good loads, which in turn benefits other members.

Ideally, rates should be based on the cost of serving consumers. A cost of service study can determine this starting point. It gives management and the board a rational basis for determining rates and demonstrates to members that rates are fair. Cost of service has been accepted by courts and commissions as an important measure of the reasonableness of a utility's rates, and experts generally agree on what constitutes cost of service. A sound cost of service study can also support a co-op's plan for rotating patronage capital by showing how much each class of consumers contributes to **margin,** (revenues in excess of costs). If a cooperative wants to offer special rates to encourage off-peak use, for instance, the cost of service study helps set discounts and incentives that are fair to all consumers.

The first step in the cost of service study is to determine **revenue requirements** based on a specific **test period**. A cooperative that is not regulated by a state commission can probably use its budget period and actual revenue and expense figures. A cooperative that is regulated will normally use a test year—historic, projected, or a combination—established by its commission. In either case, the co-op must estimate its total expenses based on normal operating conditions, such as weather and business conditions with adjustments for known changes, such as wage increases. The expenses include a margin sufficient to maintain the co-op's financial health and to meet its mortgage requirements. Historically, TIER and equity goals have been the primary considerations in establishing revenue requirements. Systems may also consider new performance requirements established by RUS, CFC and other lenders, which emphasize cash flow.

FIGURE 14.1. Classification of Costs

	Classification		
	Demand	Energy	Customer
Production	X	X	
Transmission	X		
Distribution	X		X
General			X

(Rows labeled under "Function": Production, Transmission, Distribution, General)

The next step is to **functionalize** costs, that is, to allocate the costs to specific functions, based on plant, including production, transmission, distribution, and general facilities. The cooperative's Continuing Property Records (CPR) can be used to help allocate the costs. RUS has established a CPR system for its borrowers that provides a detailed record of the cost, including materials, labor, and overhead, as well as location, description, and number of units of the property comprising the cooperative's electric plant.

Once costs are assigned to a function, they are classified as demand, energy, or consumer-related costs. Demand costs are those costs related to the investment in facilities and the demand upon the system's total capacity to serve. These costs include such items as interest on borrowed funds, taxes, and depreciation. Energy costs, on the other hand are the variable costs connected with the operation of the facility and include expenses and fuel. Consumer-related costs are the fixed costs incurred in serving each customer, including meter reading, billing, and collecting. Costs may also be directly assigned to classifications based on a specific use such as security lights or service to individual large customers. This is a crucial step in determining ultimate rate design.

The final step is to allocate the costs to specific classes of consumers. Typical consumer groups include residential, small commercial and industrial, large commercial and industrial, and irrigation customers.

Energy costs are easy to allocate: they show up as kilowatt-hour sales. Demand costs are usually based on each class's contribution to peak demand, as determined by the power supplier. The allocation of consumer-related costs is more complex and must take into account differences in service levels and other, less exact factors. Once a cooperative determines the cost of service to each of its consumer classifications, it is ready to focus on rate design.

RATE DESIGN ISSUES

Ideally, each consumer class should pay its total cost of service. However, other factors must often be considered in setting and designing rates. One such factor is value of service, the value a consumer sees in receiving a service. Consumers will not pay more for a service than they believe it is worth. They will either do without or look for a substitute. This is not an easy factor to measure, because it rests on the consumer's own opinion of what service is worth and can vary widely among consumers and consumer classes as well as from time to time and place to place.

Market forces and competitive conditions are among the most important factors in gauging value of service. For example, the average co-op residential consumer uses about 1,000 Kwh per month. About 40 percent of that goes to heating, cooling, and water heating, for which alternative sources of energy, such as liquid propane gas, are available. A cooperative that sets rates based solely on cost of service without regard to the price of alternatives is likely to lose load if its prices are higher. Some cooperatives have solved this problem by establishing special rates to retain these key heating loads. Of course, when one consumer class pays less than its full cost of service, others must make up the difference—and they, too, will be considering value of service.

Quality of service may also be an issue. Regulatory commissions and courts place as much weight on a utility's obligation to provide adequate service as they do on its right to charge reasonable rates. A regulated cooperative that provides poor service may find that to be a consideration in rate decisions. An unregulated cooperative may face strong member opposition to rate increases if the quality of service is unsatisfactory.

Rate schedules must also be easy to understand. While economic theory may dictate complex designs, good member relations dictates simplicity. Simplified structures are also easier and less costly to administer. Many cooperatives find it helpful to review rate structures periodically in their monthly newsletters or through other member communications.

Marginal Costs

Cost of service studies are based on historical costs. A rate design based on that type of study will reflect **embedded costs**, or money already invested in plant plus operating expenses. In recent years, many attempts at rate reform have focused on **marginal costs**, or **incremental costs**. The marginal cost is the cost of producing and distributing the next unit of electricity. The theory of marginal cost pricing says that utilities will operate most efficiently if the rate charged for the last unit of electricity consumed is equal to the cost of producing it, that is, the marginal cost. If additional facilities are needed to provide that unit of electricity, then the marginal cost should reflect costs of the added investment.

Although most economists agree on the theory, the practical feasibility of applying marginal cost principles to utilities is difficult. Utilities are very complex and make investments to provide a variety of functions, including generation, transmission, distribution, and service. Power costs vary with the time of day and time of year. Short-term marginal costs may differ from long-term marginal costs. Deciding which costs and which output to measure is a considerable undertaking.

A rate design based on a cost-of-service study will apportion responsibility based on the past. But who should pay the cost of new capacity? While the use of marginal cost pricing is an attempt to provide an answer to that question, implementation of such a method of rate design raises a number of complex issues. Both marginal and embedded costs can be used in setting rates.

Elasticity of Demand

Elasticity of demand refers to a consumer's ability to change his demand for service in response to price. A consumer who uses less electricity when the price increases—or more when the price goes down—has an elastic demand. A greater change reflects greater elasticity.

Cooperative consumers have demonstrated some elasticity of demand. The average monthly consumption by residential consumers increased every year from 1948 to 1978, when it reached 937 Kwh. Average revenue per kilowatt-hour fell steadily until 1970, when rates began to increase, reaching 3.80 cents per Kwh in 1978. Average monthly usage then started to slide to a low of 896 Kwh in 1983, as the average rate rapidly increased to 6.66 cents per Kwh—an average cost increase of almost 12 percent per year. Average monthly usage did not reach the 1978 level again until 1988 when it reached 951 Kwh per month. During the 1983-88 period, the average cost increased at a more moderate rate of about two percent per year to 7.31 cents per Kwh. In 1994 average usage was 1,005 Kwh per month at a cost of 7.74 cents per Kwh.

By recognizing the elasticity of member demand, a cooperative can set up rates to help change their consumption patterns. Higher on-peak rates, lower off-peak rates, or both, can spread out consumer demand. Since most co-op wholesale power bills combine charges based on peak demand with rates for power actually used, such consumption shifts can lower total system costs and keep all members' rates down.

RATE STRUCTURES

The most common residential rate structure in use today is the block meter rate. Most cooperative systems include a customer charge or minimum monthly charge designed to recover most if not all of the expense of serving the customer. There is an additional charge for each kilowatt-hour consumed, which varies across blocks of usage. The rate may increase, decrease, or remain essentially flat across the blocks of usage. For example, the basic residential rate structure of Wake Electric Membership Corporation in Wake Forest, North Carolina has a facilities charge for single-phase service of $9 per month. The first 750 kilowatt-hours are priced at 10.6 cents per Kwh. Any additional kilowatt-hours are priced at 9.88 cents per Kwh. This is a declining block schedule. If the first 750 kilowatt-hours

FIGURE 14.2. Residential Energy Consumption and Revenue/Kwh

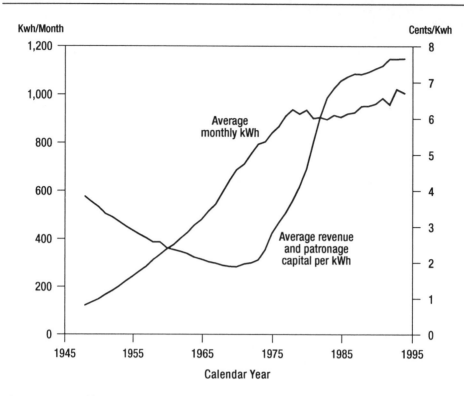

The average monthly energy used by residential consumers has increased 10.0 percent since 1984; the average revenue per Kwh has increased 12 percent during the same period. Figure 14.2 shows the average revenue per Kwh for residential consumers for the years 1948 through 1994.

SOURCE: *Rural Utilities Service, 1995*

were priced at 9.88 cents with any additional kilowatt-hours priced at 10.6 cents, it would be an inverted, or increasing, block schedule. If each kilowatt-hour cost the same amount, it would be a flat block rate. The main advantages of block meter rates are simplicity of application and member understanding.

However, a cooperative may also offer a variety of rate schedules to reflect varying end-uses or to encourage certain consumption patterns. Special rates can be used to retain heating, air conditioning, or water heating loads. The co-op may encourage conservation by offering a reduced rate to residential consumers who install insulation or burn wood or other fuel to help heat their homes. It may reward changes in usage patterns through time-of-use rates.

Cooperatives may also add surcharges reflecting changes in the cost of purchased power, state and local taxes, or special environmental costs.

TIME-OF-USE RATES—EVERYBODY SAVES

When Wake Electric Membership Corporation in Wake Forest, North Carolina introduced new rate schedules in November 1993, the cooperative offered new time-of-use rates to homeowners and small businesses. The rates give members the opportunity to save money on their power bills and help the co-op cut the cost of wholesale power.

The residential schedule has a monthly facilities charge of $13.50 for single-phase service and $26.50 for three-phase service. Kilowatt-hours consumed on-peak cost 28.5 cents, while off-peak rates are 6.25 cents per kilowatt-hour. On-peak hours are 6:00 a.m. to 10:00 a.m. Monday through Friday during the winter period from October 16 to April 30 and 2:00 p.m. to 7:00 p.m. during the summer period from May 1 to October 15. All other hours and eight holidays are off-peak hours. A member that signs up for the time-of-use schedule agrees to stay on the schedule for at least one year but can opt to return to the standard schedule by paying a $20 fee to cover part of the cost of changing the meters.

Several hundred members have elected to try the new schedule. Any member that can shift residential chores to the off-peak hours can save money, and most consumers can break even just by controlling their water heater. Other suggestions from the co-op include using programmable thermostats on heating and cooling systems, doing laundry before or after on-peak periods, and turning the dishwasher on before watching the 10:00 p.m. news.

From the co-op's standpoint, about 50 percent of its wholesale power costs are driven by demand, so its saves about half the cost of power—which represents two-thirds of its retail rate—for each kilowatt-hour removed from the peak. Most of the savings are passed along to the consumer. While the billing demand is based on the peak hour of the peak day of the month, the difficulty in predicting the peak hour and the possibility of creating a new peak if load patterns are only slightly changed, make it necessary to adopt the longer peak billing periods.

For power generators, one of the largest uncertainties in projecting costs is the cost of fuel. Fuel prices can vary significantly over time. When fuel costs were rising rapidly in the early 1970s, many power suppliers added a fuel adjustment clause to their rates to cover such unexpected increases. This provides a significant advantage when fuel costs increase rapidly because it ensures that revenues will cover the increased fuel costs. When fuel costs drop, savings can be passed along immediately. Many distribution systems, in turn, include a purchased power adjustment clause in their rate schedules to cushion themselves against such changes in their wholesale power costs.

Consumers often object to these adjustment clauses for several reasons. Since the change is automatic, some consumers argue that it reduces incentives to obtain the lowest fuel price. There may be a lag between the cause of a fuel cost increase and the appearance of the increase on power bills, which can further confuse consumers. In addition, many consumers don't like surcharges. As inflation rates have eased, and precipitous changes in costs have decreased, some cooperatives have chosen to eliminate their purchased power adjustments for the sake of better member relations.

Impact of PURPA on Rate Design

The Public Utility Regulatory Policies Act of 1978 (PURPA) imposed new objectives on utility rate making procedures. These resulted in differential charges for reasons not necessarily connected with traditional cost of service. PURPA required that regulatory policies promote four objectives: conservation, efficiency, equitable retail electric rates, and equitable rates for natural gas consumers. It also addressed issues of distribution, reliability, and wholesale electric rates.

Some states objected that the federal government was usurping their authority over electric rate making. In 1982, the U.S. Supreme Court upheld the law, ruling that PURPA did not give the federal government the power to make final utility rate decisions but rather established broad national energy policy goals. One way or another, through their state commissions or REA, most co-ops came to feel the impact of PURPA on their ratesetting policies.

The law required state regulators to consider ratemaking procedures in light of the law's four main objectives, but the state commissions would make final decisions on whether the pricing techniques they approved contributed to the national goals. PURPA also specified six ratesetting techniques that commissions should consider in terms of the law's national goals:

- Cost of service. Regulators should re-examine whether utility rates accurately reflected the cost of serving each class of consumer.

- Declining blocks. Environmental and consumer groups had charged that the tail rate, or last and lowest rate block on a utility's rate schedule, favored large consumers.

- Time-of-day rates. By increasing rates during the hours of peak use, these rates try to spread the electric load more evenly throughout the day to make more efficient use of generators and reduce the need for additional peaking capacity. PURPA supporters warned, however, that such rate differentials could send utilities chasing the peak around the clock. They also complained that time-of-day rates need special meters, driving up costs and complicating administration. PURPA allowed states to consider such rates only when they were clearly cost effective.

- Seasonal rates. Such rates apply incentives similar to those of time-of-day rates, but seek to shift use during seasonal peaks, such as summer cooling or winter heating. Again, PURPA requires cost justification for such incentives.

- Interruptible rates. Consumers can get a rate break if they agree to allow the utility to curtail service as the system nears its peak. Such rate schedules have been available to high-volume natural gas consumers for years; PURPA required consideration of such rates for commercial and industrial electric consumers.

- Load management techniques. PURPA called for consideration of rates aimed at managing system loads. Time-of-day, seasonal, and interruptible rates are load management techniques, but the law included this as a separate category as well.

CHAPTER 15

OTHER FEDERAL REGULATION

Generally, the federal government leaves regulation of intrastate activities—those which do not cross state lines—to state authorities. But since a state commission's jurisdiction stops at the border, Washington steps in to provide uniform regulation of interstate activities. As a result, some electric cooperatives may find some of their business activities falling under the regulatory jurisdiction of federal commissions as well as RUS.

The federal commissions regulate compliance with federal law, but they operate independently from other branches of government. Once appointed by the president, and confirmed by the Senate, commissioners are free to exercise independent judgment on matters coming before them, subject only to review or correction by the appellate courts. Members of a commission may and often do disagree among themselves, in which case the majority rules. Congress can abolish a commission, or change its name or duties. But neither the president nor the Congress can tell a commission how to decide a case before it.

Like their state-level counterparts, federal commissions combine the legislative, executive, and judicial functions of the three branches of government. At the federal level, however, these regulatory agencies are considered "administrative commissions" and are housed and budgeted in the executive branch.

A commission, whether federal or state, can exercise only the powers specified in the law that created it. Most commission laws state in broad terms the objectives and standards the legislators intended, leaving the commissions to work out the rules, procedures, and day-to-day mechanics of carrying out the law's intent.

The federal commissions most likely to take an interest in cooperative activities are the five-member Federal Energy Regulatory Commission, which oversees interstate and wholesale power transactions and licenses hydroelectric projects, and the five-member Nuclear Regulatory Commission (NRC), which licenses and monitors nuclear power plants.

Cooperatives that raise money through the sale of bonds must register with the five-member Securities and Exchange Commission (SEC). The SEC also keeps track of a handful of utility holding companies, whose subsidiaries may be wholesale suppliers to co-ops.

The Department of Energy

Although the idea of a Cabinet-level department to keep tabs on fuel stocks and production and to coordinate national energy policy goes back to the 1960s, the Department of Energy was not established until 1977. The department's responsibilities cover the full range of energy issues: generation and transmission of electricity; ensuring adequate supplies of gas, oil, and coal; research and development of new energy technologies; conservation measures; and environmental protection. The department has several divisions, including the Federal Energy Regulatory Commission (FERC), that bear directly on the electric industry.

The Energy Information Administration (EIA), a branch of DOE, collects virtually all the government's statistics on energy production and use. It does not have to obtain the approval of any other DOE official when collecting and analyzing data and preparing reports required by law. The EIA does, however, respond to requests for information from other parts of DOE.

The Economic Regulatory Administration (ERA) administers many of DOE's regulatory programs, including oil allocation and import programs, coal conversion, and regional coordination of electric power system planning and reliability. The ERA also intervenes before FERC on behalf of the DOE.

The Federal Energy Regulatory Commission

FERC is the successor to the Federal Power Commission (FPC). As such, it exercises substantial authority over the structure and operations of the electric industry.

The FPC was created by the Federal Water Power Act of 1920. It was given limited authority to grant a hydroelectric license to anyone wishing to build a dam across a navigable river to generate electricity. The original law was a compromise between those who wanted only the federal government itself to build and operate such dams and those who wanted to give the electric companies a free hand, subject only to state regulation.

The law did not provide for general regulation of rates or services by the hydro licensees, unless the state in which a project was located failed to exercise such powers. The FPC was essentially a part-time commission, composed of three Cabinet secretaries who already had more than enough to do running their own departments. It soon became clear that this structure was unworkable.

In 1930, the Federal Power Commission was upgraded to an independent agency with five full-time members. In 1935, it was given greatly expanded jurisdiction over the interstate commerce activities of electric utilities involving both hydro and steam facilities. Its areas of responsibility included:

- interconnection and coordination of facilities

- mergers, consolidations, sale of property, and stock issues (if otherwise unregulated within the states)

- interstate wholesale rates for power

- service adequacy upon complaint of a state commission

- property cost assessments for interstate utilities

- interstate utility accounting practices

- service abandonment

- other study and investigative duties

The Natural Gas Act of 1938 gave the FPC powers over natural gas production and transmission similar to its extensive powers over interstate electric operations.

Questions about the commission's authority to regulate gas and other issues were settled in 1977 when Congress completely reorganized the federal government's regulatory control, not only over interstate gas and electric utilities but also over other forms of energy, together with related research and development. The Federal Power Commission went out of existence on October 1, 1977, and was succeeded by the Federal Energy Regulatory Commission (FERC).

The FERC's five members are appointed by the president and confirmed by the Senate. As an independent agency within DOE, the FERC exercises wide powers which it inherited from the old Federal Power Commission, plus new duties given to it by the National Energy Act of 1978. FERC is responsible for regulating a wide range of interstate gas and electricity activities:

- Rates and services

- Licensing or issuing certificates for such services (including cogeneration facilities, small power producers, and independent power producers)

- Service curtailment or abandonment

- Mergers and stock issues

- Licensing hydroelectric projects

- Oil pipeline rates

FERC also coordinates with DOE's nonregulatory agencies on such tasks as preparing, collecting, and analyzing reports on electric power system planning, coal conversion, energy research and development, and conservation and environmental concerns. FERC's major responsibilities with respect to electric utility rate standards are spelled out in the National Energy Act of 1978.

In recent years, FERC has issued a series of orders that separated natural gas transmission and distribution. On March 29, 1995, FERC issued a Notice of Proposed Rulemaking (NOPR) seeking comments on proposals that would have similar effects on the electric industry, leading to a far more competitive wholesale power market.

Federal vs. State Jurisdiction

The federal commissions were created not to weaken the state commissions but to oversee interstate transactions that exceed state jurisdictions. However, federal regulation of utilities has occasionally raised questions of jurisdiction and points of conflict between federal and state regulators. As federal regulation has evolved, the tendency has been toward centralized federal control.

FERC has the authority to license hydroelectric developments on navigable streams. The U.S. Supreme Court has in a series of decisions extended federal control even to the tributaries of navigable streams or those which ever were or ever could be made navigable.

Where there has been a conflict between state and federal regulation, federal authority has generally taken precedence. The Supreme Court has ruled that jurisdiction over the wholesale transmission of electricity is under federal regulatory authority in nearly every case that reached the high court. One result is that the FERC pre-empts the states in setting policy for wheeling and transmission systems for cogeneration projects and independent power producers. FERC's proposed rule on promoting wholesale competition acknowledges the need to sort out which facilities are under FERC jurisdiction and which are under state jurisdiction when electric services are unbundled.

The National Energy Act of 1978

The federal government also affects the electric industry through legislation passed by Congress. A prime example is the National Energy Act of 1978 which had a significant impact on the nation's energy policy. The law consists of five statutes:

- Powerplant and Industrial Fuel Use Act. This statute sought to curtail industry's use of oil by requiring substitution of other fuels (essentially coal). The law required that new power plants and industrial boilers be capable of burning coal or alternate fuels as their primary energy source. In May 1987, President Reagan signed legislation that repealed certain restrictions imposed by the Fuel Use Act against burning natural gas or oil in industrial boilers and peak or intermediate load power plants. Those amendments reflected a re-evaluation of the nation's natural gas supplies.

- Public Utility Regulatory Policies Act (PURPA). In addition to requiring state regulators to consider four broad national energy goals, PURPA required that utilities buy power at equitable rates from cogenerators, or nonutility businesses that generate power as a by-product of some other industrial process. PURPA also granted FERC limited authority to require that one utility allow another to transmit power over its lines, a concept known as **wheeling**. This part of the law was designed to promote the efficient use of electric facilities and improve the reliability of utility systems. Similarly, the law also contained provisions designed to stimulate small hydroelectric power projects. DOE was authorized to establish a loan program to foster the development of such facilities.

- National Energy Conservation Policy Act. This law sought to foster conservation by establishing general guidelines for state conservation programs and energy audits. It also required DOE to establish efficiency standards for 13 major residential appliances and authorized grants to defray conservation expenses incurred by public and nonprofit schools and hospitals.

- Natural Gas Policy Act. This law revised the manner in which natural gas was priced. Traditionally, federal regulation had kept the price artificially low. The act provided for increased prices for "new" gas (gas discovered after April 20, 1977) and for the gradual deregulation of gas prices. One of the law's provisions, incremental pricing, was repealed in May 1987. That provision was designed to shift the cost of gas, when it was increasing, to industrial customers. As natural gas continued to drop in price, that pricing provision became a measure without economic benefit.

- Energy Tax Act. The Energy Tax Act sought to provide additional conservation incentives by allowing consumers a tax deduction for home improvements designed to conserve energy, allowing utilities to write off geothermal well depletion, and imposing a modified automobile gas guzzler tax. The tax deductions allowed by this legislation expired December 31, 1985.

Energy Policy Act of 1992

In 1989, President Bush proposed a comprehensive National Energy Strategy to build on the National Energy Act and make future energy use more efficient, less vulnerable to disruption, and environmentally safe. The Energy Policy Act of 1992 (EPAct) included many of the proposals contained in the National Energy Strategy. The legislation emphasized conservation and energy efficiency and included the following key elements affecting electric and gas utilities:

- Amendment of the Public Utility Holding Company Act of 1935. EPAct gave FERC sole authority to approve **exempt wholesale generators** (EWGs), which are not subject to PUHCA regulation. It allows exempt and registered **holding companies** to own EWGs and permits affiliate transactions, subject to state approval. The legislation also permits U.S. utility **affiliates** to participate in foreign markets, including foreign retail sales.

- Transmission Access. The EPAct amended section 211 of the Federal Power Act, enabling any entity generating wholesale electricity to make a request for FERC to order transmission service by a utility, including expansion of those facilities if needed. The legislation also expanded FERC's authority to order such wheeling. FERC was prohibited, however, from ordering retail wheeling to ultimate consumers.

- Alternate Fuel Vehicles. EPAct authorized a joint 10-year private/government demonstration program for electric vehicles, a five-year infrastructure program for electric vehicles, and a five-year research and development program on electric vehicle technology, including advanced batteries. More than $60 million was appropriated for electric vehicle programs in 1993. The law also included tax credits and deductions for investments in electric and other clean fuel vehicles. State and federal governments are required to begin including alternative fuel vehicles in their fleets.

- Nuclear Licensing Reform. The law streamlined the nuclear licensing process to combine the construction and operation proceedings.

- Global Climate Change. EPAct included provisions to encourage voluntary reductions in the emission of greenhouse gases and required DOE to establish a national inventory of such emissions.

- Energy Conservation Rebates. After 1992, 100 percent of a utility's conservation payments to residential consumers is excluded from federal taxation; for industrial and commercial consumers, 40 percent is excluded in 1995, 50 percent in 1996, and 65 percent beginning in 1997.

- Import/Export Regulation. EPAct relaxed regulation of natural gas imports and exports involving countries with free trade agreements in effect.

Environmental Legislation
The benefits of industrialization have come at significant cost to the planet's air, water, and land resources. The environmental movement that began in the 1960s fostered a public awareness of this damage. It focused attention on the fact that the price of most goods and services, including electricity, did not reflect the value of free goods, such as the air which was being filled with gaseous emissions and the waters which were being polluted with waste products.

The federal government responded to these concerns with a series of environmental laws, including the National Environmental Policy Act, the Clean Air Act, the Federal Water Pollution Control Act, Federal Lands Policy and Management Act, the Resource Conservation and Recovery Act, and the Clean Air Act Amendments of 1990.

National environmental policy has taken two approaches. One is the regulation of activities that affect environmental quality directly, especially the discharge of waste and pollutants into the environment. The other is a process of disclosure, review, comment, and public participation that is intended to affect decision making about less direct and obvious environmental impacts.

The regulation of resources that were once considered free has been costly for utilities. As much as 30 percent of the cost of a generating plant may go to pollution control equipment. The construction period for most plants has been extended due to the regulatory process, which contributes to the cost increase. Today, the price paid by the consumer for most goods and services, including electricity, includes some compensation for environmental protection.

National Environmental Policy Act
The National Environmental Policy Act of 1969 (NEPA), signed into law by President Nixon on January 1, 1970, resulted from growing public concern over the deteriorating state of the environment. Its primary purpose was to force full disclosure of the potential environmental consequences of a proposed action, thus alerting government officials and the public to the environmental risks involved. The law established the Environmental Protection Agency (EPA) as an

FIGURE 15.1. Major Federal Legislation Affecting Utility Facilities

General

1. National Environmental Policy Act of 1969
2. Atomic Energy Act of 1954
3. Endangered Species Act of 1973
4. National Historic Preservation Act of 1966
5. National Trails Systems Act
6. Fish and Wildlife Coordination Act
7. Wilderness Act
8. Federal Coal Mine Health and Safety Act of 1969
9. Surface Mining Control and Reclamation Act
10. Mining and Minerals Policy Act of 1970
11. Outer Continental Shelf Lands Act
12. Powerplant and Industrial Fuel Use Act of 1978, as modified by the Omnibus Budget Reconciliation Act of 1981
13. Outer Continental Shelf Lands Act Amendments of 1978
14. Toxic Substances Control Act of 1980

Air Quality

1. Clean Air Act of 1970
2. Clean Air Act Amendments of 1977
3. Clean Air Act Amendments of 1990

Water Quality

1. Rivers and Harbors Act of 1899
2. Water Quality Improvement Act of 1970
3. Federal Water Pollution Control Act
4. Coastal Zone Management Act
5. Federal Water Pollution Control Act Amendments of 1972
6. Wild and Scenic Rivers Act
7. Water Resources Planning Act
8. Marine Protection, Research, and Sanctuaries Act of 1972
9. Oil Pollution Act Amendments of 1973
10. Safe Water Drinking Act of 1974
11. Safe Water Drinking Act Amendments of 1987
12. Water Quality Act Amendments of 1987

Solid Waste

1. Resource Conservation and Recovery Act of 1976
2. Solid Waste Act

SOURCE: *Adapted and updated from Daniel C. Kasperski, "Licensing and Regulatory Affairs as an Engineering Discipline,"* Public Utilities Fortnightly *106 (3 July 1980): 29.*

independent agency charged with establishing and enforcing regulations to control pollution and protect the environment.

NEPA mandated a balancing process in which environmental costs must be weighed against economic benefits on a case-by-case basis. It required that an environmental impact statement (EIS) be prepared before undertaking major federal construction projects, and those projects crossing federal land that would significantly affect the environment. Although project sponsors, such as a G&T cooperative wishing to construct a new transmission line to be financed with an RUS loan guarantee, are often intimately involved in the EIS preparation and review, the obligations created by the law rest on federal agencies. The EIS is intended to be "predecisional," to require agencies to consider impacts, alternatives, and mitigation measures before a decision is reached to commit resources to a project. NEPA added no substantive standards to federal policy toward environmental protection; it established procedure.

In addition to RUS and EPA, agencies that issue permits to utilities or have other interactions that require an EIS are the Bureau of Land Management of the Department of Interior, the Forest Service of the Department of Agriculture, the Army Corps of Engineers, the Federal Energy Regulatory Commission, and the Department of Energy.

The Clean Air Act

While there are many sources of air pollution, EPA estimates that electric power generation accounts for almost 70 percent of all sulfur dioxide (SO_2) emissions and almost 40 percent of nitrogen oxide (NO_x) emissions. It also creates emissions of carbon dioxide (CO_2), methane, and particulate matter.

The Clean Air Act of 1970 directed the EPA to establish air quality standards for specific pollutants. The law also required that new electric generating plants comply with new source performance standards and utilize the best system of emission control that is feasible. Additionally, EPA's nonattainment program provided that no construction permits for a new plant would be issued in an area that had not met the national standards until an acceptable plan was approved by the EPA.

Although a federal statute, the act delegated much of the day-to-day responsibilities of air pollution control to the states. The law required each state to develop a state implementation plan (SIP) which would describe how areas not meeting standards would achieve air quality goals. These areas in violation of standards would be subject to more stringent federal requirements for new sources.

It became obvious that many areas would not meet national health standards by the established deadlines and that moratoriums on all new sources would cripple economic development in many areas. In response, EPA established an offset policy which was viewed as a means of allowing growth in areas not meeting air quality standards. Under the offset policy, new sources of pollutants could locate in nonattainment areas if they could reduce emission levels of those same pollutants elsewhere in the area and demonstrate net air quality benefits.

Deadlines for compliance with the Clean Air Act provisions were extended to August 31, 1988. Despite that extension, more than 70 cities still failed to meet the standards. In September 1988, the EPA imposed construction bans on many areas of Southern California and considered a similar ban in the Chicago metropolitan area. The sanction in California took effect immediately and halted all new construction of major pollution sources, including utility plants. Officials at the EPA asked Congress to revise the law so that states and cities with EPA assistance, could begin to compile accurate information on sources of pollution and develop reliable plans to reduce those emissions as quickly as possible.

The Acid Rain Puzzle
Despite improvements in air quality, there was increasing debate over what has come to be called acid rain. Within the last 20 years it has become evident that precipitation falling over the eastern United States, eastern Canada, and most of western Europe has become increasingly acidic. Such acid rain has been associated with industrial and automotive emissions of sulfur dioxide and, to a lesser extent, nitrogen oxide. Attention focused on electric generating stations and other industrial operations which burn large amounts of fossil fuel, especially coal.

Standards for coal-fired power plants include limits on the emission of sulfur. Such emissions have been controlled at some generating facilities through the use of stack gas scrubbers, a process in which the gases that result from the combustion of coal are passed through a tank containing a limestone solution. The sulfurous gases react with the limestone to form a thick sludge. In the late 1980s, Congress funded research and development of "clean coal technologies," aimed at helping power plants burn coal more cleanly and meet environmental requirements in a more cost-effective manner. But congressional efforts to protect the environment from harmful emissions did not end with research and development; in 1990, Congress passed an important package of amendments to the Clean Air Act.

Clean Air Act Amendments of 1990
After a decade of discussion, Congress completed an ambitious rewrite of the Clean Air Act in 1990. The law has had profound effects on every major industry in the United States, especially the electric utility industry. Acid rain controls are the heart of the legislation, which takes a market-based approach to regulation. The complex law is filled with mathematical formulas and multiple special exceptions. EPA's regulations for implementing the law are equally complex. Implementation is also complicated by the need to give new participants a way into the emerging competitive generation market.

Beginning in the year 1995, with the largest and dirtiest plants going first, all utility generators of sulfur dioxide and nitrogen oxide emissions receive "allowances" to continue their pollution. An allowance permits a single ton of emissions in a single calendar year. Under the new law, a power generator cannot throw or turn up the switch at any fossil fueled generating unit without sufficient allowances to cover the emissions the plant will produce. A utility that does not have enough allowances to cover the emissions from its plants must reduce operations into line with its allowances.

Operators of existing plants are not the only parties affected. Anyone wishing to build a new generating plant must also obtain enough allowances to cover that facility's expected emissions. There are four basic ways to obtain allowances for a new plant:

- buy allowances on the open market, at prices estimated to range from $300 to $1,500 per ton per year

- shut down or reduce generation from an old plant and use its allowances for the new one

- clean up an existing old plant to create extra allowances

- implement conservation and renewable energy projects

A generator can clean up a plant by either switching to lower sulfur fuel or installing pollution control technology. Compliance requires a series of technical and economic tradeoffs. Switching fuels may be cheaper in the short term, and it may buy time, but it may not reduce emissions as much as may be necessary in the future. Scrubbers can reduce sulfur dioxide emissions by up to 95 percent, but all scrubbers are not alike. One may cost more to build, but less to operate. Additionally, the ability to buy, sell, trade or auction their emissions allowances will significantly affect a particular utility's choices.

The allowance system's goal is to cap future sulfur dioxide emissions at 8.9 million tons annually, starting in 2000; this cap represents a 10 million ton annual reduction from 1980 emissions levels. The Clean Air Act amendments include an elaborate series of formulas for calculating the allowances that various types of utility units will receive. The sulfur dioxide allowance program is divided into two phases. Phase I runs from the beginning of 1995 to the end of 1999 and covers the largest and dirtiest plants. Phase II begins in 2000 and applies to all "utility generating units."

Exempted from the emissions limit are:

- units with a capacity of 25 MW or less

- units that cogenerate steam and electricity, unless the unit supplies more than one-third of its potential capacity and more than 25 MW of output to a utility for resale

- some small power production facilities or qualifying cogenerators and certain independent power producers

To be exempt, a power sales agreement must have been executed, the facility must be subject to a state regulatory authority order that requires an electric utility to enter into a power sales agreement, an electric utility must have issued a letter of intent in which it commits to purchase power from the facility, or the facility must be a winning bidder in a utility's competitive bid solicitation.

In addition to the special treatment applicable to small units, the law contains several important provisions that apply to joint owners of power plants. Some cooperatives own a minority interest in a fossil fueled power plant operated by another utility. The new law provides that an affected unit shall not receive a permit until the "designated representative" of the owners or operators has filed a "certificate of representation" concerning the holding and distribution of allowances. The certificate must indicate that the designated representative will hold or distribute the allowance on behalf of each owner in proportion to that entity's share of the unit, unless the owners agree otherwise.

Concerned that utilities with large amounts of "clean" fossil fueled capacity might hoard allowances, Congress built two responses into the new law: First, antitrust laws specifically apply to the use and sale of allowances. Utilities suspected of anticompetitive behavior may be charged under antitrust laws. Second, the law established an auction, to be funded by withholding 2.8 percent of allowances allocated to utilities in both phases of the program. Beginning in 2000 and annually thereafter, allowances will be auctioned off by EPA.

The clean air legislation adopted by Congress in 1990 will have far reaching implications for electric consumers. It has been estimated that compliance with the acid rain portion of the bill alone will cost electric consumers $5 billion to $7 billion a year. In this particular instance, RUS's NEPA requirements worked to the cooperatives' advantage. A number of systems were required to install scrubbers and other pollution control equipment that they might otherwise not have installed. As a result, their plants are already in compliance.

In 1995, 111 electric generating units, representing more than 93,000 MW of capacity, were subject to reductions in emissions. Investor-owned utilities own and operate 92 of those 111 units; the other 19 are operated by electric cooperatives and public power agencies. Most of those units are located in Indiana, Kentucky, Ohio, Pennsylvania, Illinois, Missouri, and West Virginia.

The Global Warming Debate

Although considerable scientific uncertainty remains, many researchers believe that manmade increases in carbon dioxide and other gases will cause a slow but significant warming of the earth's atmosphere over the next century or so by trapping solar radiation reflected off the earth's surface. That phenomenon has been termed the **greenhouse effect** and the leading greenhouse gases include water vapor, carbon dioxide, methane, chlorofluorocarbons, and nitrous oxide. The United Nations Intergovernmental Panel on Climate Change (IPCC) estimates that between 1980 and 1990, carbon dioxide accounted for over half of the heat trapped; chlorofluorocarbons, 24 percent; methane, 15 percent; and nitrous oxide, 6 percent. Energy production and use was responsible for about 45 percent of the heat trapped over the decade. The IPCC says that the average global temperature has increased one-half to one degree Fahrenheit in the last hundred years.

About a quarter of greenhouse emissions are produced by the combustion of fossil fuels in the United States. This U.S. share comes in approximately equal proportions from industrial processes, electric power production, and transportation, with homes and businesses playing a smaller part.

The possible effects of global warming include a rise in sea levels, deforestation, shifts in agricultural productivity, and changing patterns of disease resulting in loss of life. Policy makers have taken three basic positions in the emerging greenhouse policy debate: more research is needed before we can respond effectively; climate change is inevitable and we should adapt; we should start immediately to mitigate the changes.

A 1995 EPA study reduced previous estimates for global warming by the year 2100 by half to about 3.6 degrees Fahrenheit. It estimates a 50-50 chance of a sea levels rising by six inches by 2050 and about a foot by 2100. IPCC projects an increase in average global temperature of 1.8 to 6.3 degrees Fahrenheit by 2100. In the past, even smaller changes in average temperature have resulted in ice ages and warm-ups.

The major policy options for slowing the buildup of greenhouse gases include reducing emissions, reducing tropical deforestation, and limiting the combustion of fossil fuels.

In December 1987, the Global Climate Protection Act of 1987 became law, requiring the president, through the EPA, to propose to Congress a national policy in this area. In June 1992, representatives of 150 nations, including the United States, signed the United Nations Framework Convention on Climate change at the first Earth Summit in Rio de Janeiro. The nations agreed to cooperate to stabilize greenhouse gases in the atmosphere.

The United States has adopted a voluntary approach to solving the problem. In 1995, President Clinton set a goal of reducing U.S. greenhouse emissions to 1990 levels by the year 2000, but some critics complained he didn't go far enough and called for reducing emissions to 20 percent below 1990 levels by 2005. The president's plan entails federal expenses of $1.9 billion by 2000.

In 1994, electric utility trade associations reached an agreement with DOE on the Climate Challenge Program, a voluntary effort to reduce emissions. More than 800 utilities representing more than 80 percent of U.S. generating capacity have made specific commitments to reduce or remove greenhouse gases. DOE is also working with the utilities to develop voluntary emissions reporting procedures.

Electric utilities have also begun to look at how a global warming trend might affect them: the effects of projected temperature rise on heating and air conditioning loads and the implications of reduced stream flow for hydro operations being two of those effects.

Natural Gas and the Environment

These days natural gas is the fuel of choice for many policy makers concerned about the environment. Natural gas causes less pollution than burning coal or fuel oil. Gas produces virtually no sulfur dioxide, a primary precursor to acid rain, or ash. Scrubbers can remove 95 percent of the sulfur dioxide produced by a coal plant, but they also produce large amounts of waste which must be disposed of, and they reduce plant efficiency. Natural gas powered plants can be designed to emit significantly lower levels of nitrous oxides than other fossil-fueled plants. Natural gas plants emit 30 percent less carbon dioxide, the major greenhouse gas, than oil combustion and 45 percent less than coal combustion on an equivalent energy basis. Finally, gas-fired combined-cycle technology is the most efficient technology available today.

Electromagnetic Fields

A 1979 study of childhood cancer in Denver linked the development of childhood leukemia to exposure to electromagnetic fields (EMF) from power lines located near the children's homes. The study was subject to much debate and criticism, but it also sparked the interest of scientists. Researchers have also studied occupational exposure to EMF. The issue gained national attention with the publication of a controversial series of articles in the New Yorker magazine in 1989 which highlighted the 1979 study. The article was widely criticized, but it raised concerns among citizens throughout the country.

To date, study results have been inconsistent and have not established a clear relationship between EMF and disease. They have, however, suggested possible links to increased risk of leukemia and brain cancer. The University of North Carolina at Chapel Hill in 1995 released results of a study of 139,000 people who worked at five utilities between 1950 and 1986. The study, sponsored by the Electric Power Research Institute, found that the overall death rate from cancer was 86 percent of that of the general population. The study found no link between EMF exposure and leukemia but did find that workers with high EMF exposure had more than twice as many brain cancer deaths as those with low EMF exposure.

A 1994 study of workers at French and Canadian utilities found that workers with a high exposure to EMF had more than 12 times the risk of dying of leukemia than workers with a low exposure. On the other hand, a 1993 study of workers at Southern California Edison Co. found no increased risk of either leukemia or brain cancer. So far, researchers are unable to explain the differences in these and other studies, and they do not know whether EMF causes cancer. Nor can the results of the occupational studies be transferred to potential risks from exposure in other work places or the home.

In 1994, a Washington state workers compensation appeals board rejected a 1991 claim by the widow of a former employee of Seattle City Light that her husband's leukemia was caused by EMF exposure. The board found that it had no legal basis for paying the claim, given the lack of a proven cause-and-effect relationship between EMF exposure and the disease.

In September 1995, 14 scientists, including six Nobel laureates, joined the American Medical Association and the California Medical Association in filing briefs with the California Supreme Court in an EMF suit involving San Diego Gas & Electric Co. The scientists said that "physics and cellular biology combined strongly indicate that it is not scientifically reasonable to believe that magnetic fields [EMF] increase the incidence of cancer." In a joint brief, the medical associations said that "...no scientifically documented health risk has been associated with the usually occurring levels of electromagnetic fields."

Whatever the final conclusions on this issue, the level of risk does not appear significant compared to other risks that are found acceptable in everyday life. Some utilities and regulators have adopted a policy of prudent avoidance in siting electrical lines, substations, and other facilities to minimize the public's exposure to electrical and magnetic fields. People who are concerned about EMF in the home can make similar changes in their habits and use of electrical appliances to eliminate unnecessary exposure.

Water Pollution Legislation
Electric utilities are significantly affected by water pollution laws. Almost half of all water used in the United States is employed for cooling and condensing, and electric utilities account for 80 percent of that.

One of the most basic requirements of electric generation is water. Thermal plants require large amounts of water for dissipating waste heat, the heat not used to turn the steam turbines. This heat is eventually dissipated into the atmosphere, and a convenient way to do that is by using water to disperse it. Chemicals are often introduced into the cooling water to prevent the growth of algae in the cooling system, and these additives are potential pollutants. Direct use of lakes, streams, or oceans or cooling can affect fish and other animals.

The nation's efforts to control water pollution date from 1972 when the Federal Water Pollution Control Act was passed. This law was a massive effort calling for the reduction and elimination of water pollution from both municipal sewage systems and industrial facilities. The law's water quality standards were to be achieved through new state and federal regulatory powers and adoption of a comprehensive permit and licensing program.

In 1977, Congress amended the Federal Water Pollution Control Act by adopting the Clean Water Act. Concentrating primarily on regulation of toxic pollutants, it eased stringent controls on conventional pollutants and extended deadlines for installing cleanup technology.

Industry had criticized EPA's application of cost-effectiveness criteria in determining whether tighter controls than "best practicable technology" (BPT) should be required for conventional pollutants. Congress in the 1977 amendments decided that the more stringent "best available technology" (BAT) standard need not be applied to some conventional pollutants and instead established the "best conventional technology" (BCT) test. The EPA, in determining the best conventional technology, must consider whether the costs of reducing the pollution matches the value of resulting benefits.

Other Environmental Legislation

Like air and water, land is used by utilities to dispose of waste from generating electricity. The Resource Conservation and Recovery Act (RCRA) determines how these residuals are to be treated and disposed of. RCRA has two subtitles that are particularly relevant to the utility industry:

- Subtitle D regulates methods for disposal of nonhazardous solid waste, fly ash, and bottom ash, which currently includes most of the solid waste produced by fossil fuel plants.

- Subtitle E creates a framework for recycling materials from power plant waste. More than 20 percent of the fly ash and bottom ash is currently reused.

Electric and gas utilities, including cooperatives, are inextricably tied to the use of land not only for siting power plants, transmission lines, pipelines, and disposal of wastes but also for the stewardship of natural resources on their property. In many cases, an electric generating station and its associated facilities occupy only a small fraction of the plant site, with natural areas maintained in the remainder. In the case of hydroelectric facilities, FERC regulations require utilities to provide recreational facilities.

Other federal initiatives such as the National Historic Preservation Act and Executive Order 11593 establish review and consultation procedures to ensure that historic and archeological resources are preserved or recorded. The Fish and Wildlife Coordination Act and the Rare and Endangered Species Act of 1973 provide for the protection of threatened and endangered species of plant and animals and their habitats.

Other laws have an impact on the industry's ability to find routes for electric and gas transmission lines where those lines must cross or bypass federal lands. These laws include the Forest and Rangeland Renewable Resources Planning Act of 1974, the National Forest Management Act of 1976, and the Federal Land Policy and Management Act of 1976. Their influence in siting utility facilities is especially strong in Western states where the federal government owns 60 percent of the land.

In addition to federal regulations and permits, most states have statutes specifically related to generating facility siting and transmission or pipeline rights of way. As utility companies add new facilities to meet demand, the siting of facilities and the laws and regulations affecting them become very important to utilities and to the public.

PART 5

COMPETITIVE STRATEGIES

CHAPTER

Strategies for Competing in a New Environment

"Clearly, this commission is not 'introducing' competition to the electricity industry. Competition has introduced itself. Marketplace economics have changed. Customers are simply demanding access to lower cost generation resources. The actions we propose today would require utilities to make their systems available to foster competition in generation. In many cases, this is a fundamental change in the historic expectations of utilities as power suppliers."

—Elizabeth A. Moler
Chair, Federal Energy Regulatory Commission
March 29, 1995

Electric cooperatives are no strangers to competition. From the earliest days of the rural electric program, they have fought with investor-owned utilities over the right to serve large power loads located in cooperative service territory. They have competed with municipal utilities to retain formerly rural areas that, due to cooperative efforts, developed into attractive suburban communities. They have gone head to head with other energy sources, competing with bottled gas, fuel, oil, and even wood for heating loads.

Today, however, new competitive forces are presenting a formidable challenge, not only to electric cooperatives, but to all publicly and privately owned utilities. Competition for customers has emerged from outside the traditional regulated utility environment, and it has become the catalyst for a major restructuring of the electric industry.

The Federal Energy Regulatory Commission (FERC) is leading a transition to market-based—rather than cost-based—rates and is taking steps to force utilities to unbundle, or offer separately, the generation, transmission, and distribution services they provide. By the fall of 1995, regulators in 38 states were investigating restructuring and competition issues. Retail competition experiments were planned in Michigan and New Hampshire.

Regulators in California have proposed the most far-reaching changes to date, calling for direct access, or retail wheeling, for all customers, to be phased in between 1998 and 2002. With rates to commercial and industrial consumers running fifty percent higher than the national average, the state believes competition will reduce power costs.

The major controversy has been whether this would be achieved through a statewide pool or by direct access through bi-lateral agreements between buyers and sellers. In September 1995, several parties, including Southern California Edison Company, the California Manufacturers Association, California Large Energy Consumers Association, and the Independent Power Producers, filed a Memorandum of Understanding (MOU) with the California Public Utilities Commission (CPUC) outlining a compromise solution proposing the simultaneous development of a power pool and direct access. While Pacific Gas & Electric Company and San Diego Gas & Electric Company were not signatories to the MOU, they, along with Southern California Edison, have expressed an intent to file a joint application with FERC in early 1996 to implement a similar proposal.

Under the compromise, power producers would form a voluntary power exchange that would manage a short-term spot market for power. An independent system operator (ISO) having no financial interest in the generation sources would be created to operate and manage the transmission system. The ISO would be responsible for scheduling transactions, providing comparable non-discriminatory access to all parties, and maintaining system reliability and safety. Customers could purchase power from the power exchange and could also enter into bi-lateral purchase contracts that would be scheduled with the ISO but not subject to the bidding or economic dispatch requirements of the power exchange.

If California implements this proposal, it could well become a model for other states. It would offer cooperatives the advantage of having access to a wider range of power sources and the disadvantage of giving other suppliers direct access to cooperative consumer-members.

Most cooperative systems are already "unbundled," with distribution service handled by individual retail co-ops that buy wholesale power from separate generation and transmission co-ops.

Changes in process or under consideration at FERC and at state commissions, however, are likely to place further competitive pressures on cooperatives—especially G&T systems. FERC in particular has focused on opening transmission facilities to produce a freer wholesale market, and there are now 44 open access transmission tariffs on file. These moves will probably give distribution systems access to lower cost bulk power, and the only thing standing between the distribution cooperatives and lower rates for their members will be their all-requirements contracts with the G&T.

Such regulatory and marketplace changes bring new business opportunities, but they also bring tremendous risks. Utilities that cannot offer competitive rates may not survive.

AEP SUPPORTS RETAIL COMPETITION

Saying that all customers should receive the benefits of competition and that customers should be free to buy electricity from anyone they choose, American Electric Power (AEP) issued a position statement in October 1995 that supported the basic concept for industry restructuring that is also under consideration in California.

AEP's proposal is based in the assumption that the generation and sale of electricity has evolved into a competitive business but that transmission and distribution should remain regulated functions. It suggests the organization of regional power exchanges where generators and resellers would offer competitive bids to meet the requirements of buyers in a spot market at half-hour intervals. At the same time, individual buyers and sellers would also have the option of entering into bi-lateral contracts. Generation additions would be built by competitors in the marketplace. Electric companies would have the option but not the obligation of undertaking new generation projects.

AEP also proposes the creation of independent system operators (ISOs) to operate transmission services in wide, multi-state regions containing many generators. The electric companies would retain ownership of their transmission but place it under the management of the ISO. The ISO would control the transmission grid and assure that all users, including those purchasing from the power exchange and through bilateral transactions, would have open access. In addition to operating the grid and providing ancillary services, the ISO would be responsible for planning additions. Services provided by the ISO would be regulated by FERC.

The existing electric companies would continue to deliver electricity to ultimate users under terms and conditions determined by state regulators. The electric companies would also purchase electricity from the power exchange for customers that did not wish to arrange for their own supply. The customers would pay the market price for electricity, which could be reflected in a monthly adjustment clause, plus a delivery fee.

Stranded costs would be recovered through a competitive access charge included in the delivery charge for both new and existing customers.

Implementation of this proposal would require additional legislative and regulatory changes.

Legislative Background

The National Energy Act of 1978 (discussed in Parts II and IV) set the stage for the competitive revolution now taking place in the utility industry.

Of the law's five sections, the Powerplant and Industrial Fuel Use Act is probably most responsible for the increased competitive pressures co-ops face today. This section of the law prohibited new generating sources from using natural gas. This restriction on fuel supply alternatives occurred just as the G&Ts were entering a decade-long construction phase. Today, about three quarters of all G&T generating capacity is coal-fired, and in some cases this reliance on coal carries serious competitive consequences.

Other parts of the 1978 law contributed to today's competitive situation as well. The Public Utilities Regulatory Policies Act granted federal regulators limited power to order wholesale wheeling and created new types of nonutility power producers, while the Natural Gas Policy Act lifted gas price controls—a step that would eventually lead to its emergence as an important industrial fuel.

Of the 1978 law's five statutes, PURPA and the Natural Gas Policy Act had the most far-reaching effect on the electric industry as a whole. The cogenerators and small power producers operating under PURPA demonstrated that generation was not necessarily a monopoly function and that nonutility generators could provide reliable, attractive sources of power. The changes triggered by the gas act ultimately transformed natural gas into a viable, in fact preferred, fuel for power generation. A vigorous independent power industry soon developed, but it was not until passage of the Energy Policy Act of 1992 (EPAct) that the major barriers to competition began to fall.

Energy Policy Act of 1992

The Energy Policy Act of 1992 (EPAct) addressed the need for a comprehensive national energy policy emphasizing conservation and energy efficiency. It removed the most significant obstacles to competition in the generation sector. The legislation was viewed by many as a Congressional endorsement of competition in the wholesale power market.

Most IPPs saw the Public Utility Holding Company Act of 1935 (PUHCA) as the greatest impediment to the development of a competitive generation market. PUHCA was enacted to stop abuses in the utility industry at a time when eight holding companies controlled more than 67 percent of the nation's electric generation. The Act defined a **holding company** as any entity owning ten percent or more of the voting securities of an electric utility, a retail gas utility, or another holding company. If a holding company holds enough of a company's common stock or other securities, it may actually control the operation of the other company and be able to direct its management with respect to policy and other decisions. In such cases, the holding company is referred to as a **parent company**, and the controlled company is called a **subsidiary**. Subsidiaries that are controlled by the same parent company are **affiliates** of each other.

Holding companies were required to register with the SEC and to submit to extensive regulation or to obtain an exemption which limited the areas in which the utility could serve and its ability to engage in other businesses.

Electric cooperatives that issue public securities, and a few have, are required to comply with the applicable regulations of the SEC. Their corporate structure is such, however, that they are not subject to PUHCA regulation.

It was extremely difficult for an IPP to qualify for exemption under the Holding Company Act. (PURPA exempted QFs from PUHCA regulation). The burdensome regulation to which holding companies were subjected limited the IPP's ability to develop and operate projects, and developers sought to avoid holding company status at all costs. This resulted in the development of contorted, inefficient corporate structures known informally as "PUHCA pretzels." The complexity of these organizations discouraged investors and also gave rise to much higher transaction costs, including fees for lawyers and accountants, than for conventional projects.

The EPAct gave FERC the authority to approve a new category of power generator, the **exempt wholesale generator** (EWG), which would not be subject to PUHCA regulation. EWGs remain subject to regulation under the Federal Power Act and applicable state laws and regulations. By the fall of 1995, 101 companies had qualified for EWG status.

A second major impediment to competitive generation was the lack of access by nonutility generators and others to adequate transmission services. Most distribution cooperatives and many G&Ts are transmission dependent utilities that must rely on transmission systems owned by other utilities to move the power from the G&T to the distribution co-op. As such, cooperatives have long supported widespread transmission access for wholesale transactions.

Transmission is a critical element of the emerging competitive power market because it determines whether a power customer has a choice of suppliers. Likewise, a generator with access to a transmission grid can offer its product to a larger geographic area—and thus more potential purchasers—than a generator with no access. Proponents of transmission access argued that for a competitive generation market to develop, suppliers had to have predictable access to transmission facilities and buyers needed to be able to negotiate with a range of suppliers.

Prior to EPAct, **wheeling**—the use of a utility's lines to transmit another supplier's power—was at the discretion of the owner of the transmission lines. Access was granted voluntarily; it could and often was denied by the line's owner to keep other suppliers out of a lucrative, and captive, market.

This posed economic problems for transmission-dependent cooperatives and other wholesale customers, as well as IPPs and other potential suppliers. Transmission-owning utilities could block cooperative access to new, competitive supplies, while the utilities owning the lines and their affiliates enjoyed access to important loads.

It is virtually impossible for cooperatives, IPPs, or other buyers and sellers to get approval for additional transmission where adequate facilities exist—and sometimes for that matter, even where new transmission is needed. Any system unable to negotiate transmission service, therefore, had no way to get lower cost power.

EPAct amended the Federal Power Act to give FERC greater authority to order wholesale transmission access, including the ability to require added capacity. The 1992 law specifically prohibited FERC from ordering retail wheeling directly to an ultimate consumer. Since passage of EPAct, however, a number of state regulatory agencies have taken up the question of retail wheeling and some have ordered retail wheeling experiments. Many industry observers believe transmission owners will be required to provide retail wheeling within a few years.

The Scope of Nonutility Generation

PURPA and EPAct have fostered a remarkable development in the nonutility generation marketplace. Although many utilities were initially skeptical about the ability of IPPs to deliver a reliable supply of power at a reasonable cost, years of experience and regulatory pressures have combined to make independent power projects a widely accepted alternative for meeting new power needs. A study by RCG/Hagler Bailly Inc., an industry data collection and consulting firm, found nonutility generators provided 53 percent of new U.S. capacity from 1990 through 1993, for a total of 33,997 MW. Many electric and gas utilities have created subsidiaries to develop independent production facilities. There are now 101 electric wholesale generators.

According to the Edison Electric Institute, the trade association for investor-owned utilities, 4,383 nonutility generating projects were producing 58,134.3 MW, or 7 percent of total U.S. capacity, by the end of 1993. Those facilities accounted for 10 percent of total U.S. electric generation in 1993. Most of them are small projects, with more than half generating one megawatt or less. The remaining plants, however, generate more than 99 percent of total nonutility capacity.

Both utilities and nonutilities saw decreased growth rates in 1993. Total nonutility capacity in the United States increased by five percent during 1993, compared to an average annual growth rate of eleven percent for the previous three years. Total industry capacity increased by less than 0.5 percent in 1993. Of the nonutility capacity that began operation in 1993, combustion turbines represented seventy percent, steam turbines twenty-two percent, internal combustion and geothermal three percent each and hydro two percent of the total. Wind and solar accounted for less than 0.5 percent. One fuel cell project began operation in 1993.

Five states accounted for half of all nonutility capacity at year end 1993: California (nineteen percent), Texas (fifteen percent), Virginia (six percent), New York (five percent), and Louisiana (five percent). In five states (Rhode Island, Maine, Hawaii, Alaska, and California, and New Hampshire), nonutility generation accounted for twenty percent or more of the total generation available in the state.

WHOLESALE VS. RETAIL WHEELING

Wholesale wheeling usually refers to transmission service provided to utilities that sell and deliver the power transmitted to end users. Retail wheeling usually refers to transmission service provided directly to end users.

Initially, most proponents of competitive generation focused on the need for transmission access for wholesale wheeling, arguing that IPPs needed the ability to wheel into competitive markets so that the siting of projects was not limited to a purchasing utility's service area. They also needed to wheel out of a particular area where an economic site could be developed but there was no need for power.

Many large industrial customers have asked for retail wheeling so that they could buy power from an alternative (and presumably lower cost) source. While the EPAct specifically prohibits FERC from ordering retail wheeling, a number of state regulatory agencies have addressed the issue, and some have ordered retail wheeling experiments. Some states, such as California, are considering ordering retail wheeling for commercial and residential loads as well as industrial loads.

Cooperatives are generally opposed to mandatory retail wheeling, because it has the potential to create a large level of stranded costs and to shift costs inequitably among consumer classes. However, many cooperatives may also be less vulnerable to losses from retail wheeling, because most of their consumers are less-attractive residential loads. Only about 40 systems serve individual loads of 25 megawatts or more, a size more likely to be attractive to competitors.

Electric utilities represent the biggest market by far for nonutility power. The Edison Electric Institute reports that ninety-eight percent of the capacity of small power producers and eighty-five percent of cogeneration capacity is interconnected with the transmission and/or distribution systems of electric utilities. Electric utilities received fifty-five percent of the power generated by nonutility generators in 1993, compared to forty percent in 1988 and eight percent in 1979. Utility purchases of 181,515 gigawatt-hours of nonutility power in 1993 represented an increase of sixteen percent from the year before. The U.S. Department of Energy projects that the United States will need 100,000 MW of new capacity in the next 10 years. The National Independent Energy Producers, an IPP trade group, reports that more than 1,400 independent power projects, representing 73,672 MW of potential capacity, are being developed. Some of these projects may not be completed, but it's clear that nonutility generators will continue to provide a significant portion of capacity additions.

FIGURE 16.1 The Status of U.S. Nonutility Generation
December 31, 1993

	Projects		Capacity		Generation
	#	%	MW	%	%
New England	614	14.0	4,752	8.2	7.3
Mid-Atlantic	608	13.9	6,984	12.0	13.0
East N. Central	427	9.7	5,195	8.9	8.6
West N. Central	250	5.7	1,186	2.0	1.7
S. Atlantic	336	7.7	9,792	16.8	16.7
East S. Central	70	1.6	2,090	3.6	3.3
West S. Central	375	8.6	12,778	22.0	22.8
Mountain	221	5.0	1,767	3.0	3.1
Pacific	1,314	30.0	12,110	20.8	21.0
Alaska & Hawaii	168	3.8	1,480	2.6	2.4
Total:	3,383	100.0%	58,134	100.0%	100.0%

SOURCE: *Edison Electric Institute*

Marketers and Brokers

Two other new players have surfaced in the wholesale electric markets. **Power marketers** purchase bulk power for resale. They take title to the power and thus become subject to FERC regulation. Marketers seek to sell their power at market-based, rather than cost-based, rates because market-based rates are potentially more profitable. In order to get FERC approval for that, the marketer must demonstrate that it lacks market power. Generally, marketers do not own generation or transmission facilities, they cannot be affiliated with a transmission owner, and they cannot be affiliated with a franchised utility. The marketer accepts the price risk of being able to resell the power and arranges for transmission. It may also bundle different types of power and services for its customers.

A few investor-owned utilities have been able to organize marketing affiliates by demonstrating in other ways that they lack or have adequately mitigated market power. In addition to utilities, finance houses, cogenerators, natural gas companies, and independent merchants have organized marketing affiliates. Between 1992 and the fall of 1995, the number of marketers approved by FERC grew from eight to 150.

Brokers—the other new players on the scene—arrange transactions between buyers and sellers and earn a commission on the deal. Since the broker does not take title to the power, it is not subject to FERC regulation. However, most brokers do not offer the range of services offered by a marketer that can also provide such amenities as bundling power from different sources, covering losses, and providing transmission. Brokers face no price risk, but they lose their commission if a transaction falls through.

CHAPTER

FERC's New Initiatives

FERC has made it clear in its rulings and in statements by individual commissioners that it supports a competitive wholesale power market, including open access transmission. Much of the commission's activity in recent years has focused on transmission issues.

Since the passage of EPAct, FERC has broadly interpreted its ability to exercise its expanded transmission authority. Historically, transmission owners were required to offer similar rates, terms and conditions to similar types of customers. EPAct shifted discrimination concerns to transmission customers who were also actual or potential competitors. In May 1994, in a case involving American Electric Power Service Corp., the commission implemented a new standard for gauging discrimination and anticompetitive behavior. The new "comparability" standard requires a transmission owner to offer third parties the same or similar use of its transmission system that it offers itself. FERC later applied comparability in rulings on mergers and requests by affiliates of power producers for market-based rates.

In October 1994, FERC issued a transmission pricing policy statement that affirmed the comparability principle and said the commission would apply it to all new transmission pricing proposals. Four additional principles were adopted, including a mandate for pricing proposals to meet traditional revenue requirements, to promote economic efficiency, to promote fairness and to be practical. The commission said it would consider pricing proposals not conforming to traditional revenue requirements model if a conforming proposal is also submitted. Questions remain as to how this policy will be applied in actual orders, but it appears that the nation's transmission system will essentially become a common carrier for electricity, much as the nation's rail lines are accessible to any railroad company.

In August 1993, FERC issued a policy statement regarding **Regional Transmission Groups** (RTGs). An RTG is a voluntary organization of transmission owners, users, and others with an interest in the use and expansion of a region's transmission facilities. Such groups would coordinate planning and attempt to resolve disputes over transmission services. FERC indicated that it would defer to decisions by RTGs to the degree that the RTG agreement mitigates the market power of transmission owners and provides a fair procedure for decision-making. As of October 1995, FERC had approved three RTGs. If the RTGs develop as anticipated, they can eliminate the need for FERC to decide many issues on a case-by-case basis and help electric suppliers do a better job of planning transmission additions.

DEREGULATION IN THE NATURAL GAS INDUSTRY

One of the Federal Energy Regulatory Commission's objectives in issuing the mega-NOPR for the electric industry was to implement proposed changes in a single step as opposed to the process that evolved over more than a decade in the natural gas industry.

The Natural Gas Act of 1938 gave the Federal Power Commission authority to regulate the sale of gas in interstate commerce for resale as well as limited franchising powers. Before 1954, the FPC regulated on the interstate natural gas pipeline companies that purchased and transported gas from producing to distributing companies. In 1954, a Supreme Court decision in Phillips Petroleum Co. v. Wisconsin found all sales by natural gas producers to interstate pipelines to be sales for resale under the Natural Gas Act and extended FPC regulation to all independent producers' sales.

The maximum allowable selling price under the Natural Gas Act was historically determined on the basis of actual production costs, not market value for the fuel. Federal regulatory practice kept the price of natural gas well below the costs of competitive fuels, thus expanding the demand for gas. By the late 1960s, industry officials and some respected economists were arguing that wellhead prices were so low that regulation was, in fact, restraining the nation's capacity to find and produce gas. In 1967, the nation's reserves began a decline that continued until 1981, when producer incentives of the Natural Gas Policy Act of 1978 began to work their course.

Because the regulated prices in the interstate market were so low relative to the market value of the gas, producers marketed new supplies of gas in the intrastate markets where prices were higher. This practice led to shortages and curtailments in nonproducing states.

The Natural Gas Policy Act of 1978 (NGPA) established a new national policy, reflecting contemporary market and supply conditions. It altered industry regulation considerably and extended price controls to intrastate gas. The act authorized FERC to oversee and administer a complex pricing policy, allocated high-priced gas for industrial use, and established price ceilings, with escalators, that were indexed for inflation.

The NGPA provided for partial and phased deregulation of natural gas prices at the wellhead, that is, the wholesale price paid to domestic producers. These pricing provisions were designed to unify the interstate and intrastate markets and to move the price of new natural gas gradually up to the equivalent of the price per barrel of oil.

Title 1 of NGPA stipulated that supplies discovered prior to April 1977 (designated "old" gas) were subject to the old price ceilings in effect before NGPA became law, and would remain under controls indefinitely, but rise monthly to keep pace with inflation. Supplies discovered after April 1977 ("new" gas) were placed on a gradual decontrol schedule, with all controls expiring in January 1985.

continued on next page

Gas prices stabilized in 1983 and began a slow decline in 1984 and 1985. The development of a spot market for gas also contributed to the decline in cost. Over time, FERC took a series of actions to unbundle, or separate, transportation services offered by interstate natural gas pipelines, to separate the merchant and transportation functions of gas pipelines, and to allow market-based rates for natural gas services by pipelines.

FERC's actions culminated in July 1991 with the issuance of a notice of proposed rulemaking on natural gas pipeline service and rate design followed by the issuance of Order No. 636 in April 1992. Order No. 636 effectively restructured the natural gas industry. The most significant issue was the treatment of interstate pipeline sales and transportation transactions. The commission noted in its order that gas pipelines have played dual roles as both merchants and transporters. It found that there was a lack of comparability between the transportation included in the pipelines' city gate firm sales service and the separately available firm transportation services that had been available since Order No. 436 mandated it in October 1985. The FERC cited the fact that in 1990 nearly two-thirds of the gas delivered for pipeline competitors was done so on an interruptible basis as evidence of the lack of comparability. To assure effective competition, FERC found that sales and transportation activities must be unbundled and priced separately.

The commission suggested that unbundling would benefit pipelines in several ways: pipelines, currently selling on a regulated basis, would be put in a better position to compete with gas merchants who generally sell uncontrolled gas. The commission deemed it natural to rely on market factors for pricing, although it was careful to point out that it was not totally deregulating pipeline sales. Instead, FERC said that it was instituting a light-handed form of regulation that would rely on decontrolled market forces to maintain rates at a reasonable level. Customers could now make their gas purchase decisions without regard to the identity of the seller.

Order No. 636 also addressed the service obligations of pipelines. It allows pipelines to abandon service, without commission review (*i.e.*, pre-granted abandonment) at contract termination except in the case of service to a firm transportation customer if the customer agrees to match the competing bidder's offer. Pre-granted abandonment also applies to storage contracts. The regulations also provide for capacity reallocation to provide both permanent and temporary releases of firm pipeline capacity. Transportation is defined to include storage service.

There are some parallels between the electric industry as it exists today and the gas industry before Order No. 436 and Order No. 636. In most cases, utilities sell bundled generation and transmission services to wholesale customers. The pattern of deregulation proposed for the electric industry in FERC's mega-NOPR is similar to that achieved in the gas industry but is being implemented in a shorter time frame.

The FERC Mega-NOPR

Using its new EPAct authority, FERC initiated a major restructuring of the electric utility industry in March 1995 when it issued a Notice of Proposed Rulemaking (NOPR) on open access transmission services, real-time information systems, and stranded costs. The proposals, collectively referred to as the mega-NOPR, would result in an electric utility industry that closely parallels the recently restructured natural gas industry.

FERC states in its orders that monopoly control of transmission is the single greatest impediment to wholesale competition. The proposed rule would require utilities under FERC jurisdiction—and those that own or control transmission facilities in interstate commerce—to file tariffs for service to third parties, to offer transmission to eligible customers comparable to the service they provide themselves, and to apply the tariffs to their own wholesale energy transmissions.

While the proposed rule does not require corporate unbundling—that is, it does not require utilities to sell assets to a non-affiliate or establish a separate affiliate to manage transmission—it does require a functional unbundling of transmission from other utility services. According to the commission, **functional unbundling** means that a utility must obtain transmission service for all of its new wholesale sales and purchases under the same tariff it applies when offering these services to others. The tariff must include separate rates for transmission and ancillary services. FERC defines ancillary services to include all services necessary to support the transmission of electric power from resources to loan while maintaining reliable operation of the transmission system. Voltage control, system protection, scheduling and dispatch, and compensation for transmission losses are examples of ancillary services. In addition, the utility must rely on the same electronic network that its customers use to obtain transmission information about its system when buying or selling power.

Historically, regulators allowed utilities to recover all of the costs they incurred to provide service to their customers. The emerging competitive market, however, will allow a customer to bypass, or leave, its electric supplier, and a utility may no longer be able to recover the costs it incurred to serve that customer. **Stranded costs** include any legitimate, prudent and verifiable costs incurred by a utility to provide service to a customer that the utility is subsequently unable to recover due to the emergence of the competitive market. For example, some investments in generation will be unrecoverable at competitive market prices. It is inevitable that such costs will occur in the transition to a competitive power industry. In its rulemaking proceedings, FERC said utilities are entitled to full recovery of legitimate and verifiable stranded costs at both the state and federal level. It said stranded costs should be directly assigned to departing wholesale customers for contracts signed before July 11, 1994. Departing customers would pay an exit fee or a surcharge in their transmission rate. No stranded cost recovery would be allowed for later contracts unless the contract specifically provided for it. FERC deferred to the states on recovery of costs stranded due to retail wheeling or direct access, except where the state regulatory agency does not have authority over such issues.

In its comments to FERC, NRECA supported the basic concept of stranded cost recovery when the stranded costs are based on basic changes in regulatory relationships but expressed concern about the impact of some aspects of the Commission's proposals on stranded costs on electric cooperatives. How a system might be affected by the proposed rules depends on its level of ownership and control of its power supply and transmission resources.

One concern is that some utilities will use stranded cost recovery to prevent wholesale customers from obtaining a new power supplier. If the charge for leaving the system is high enough, it effectively negates the benefits of competition.

FERC's working definition of stranded costs tie them to customers who subsequently become "in whole or in part, an unbundled transmission services customer of that public utility or transmitting utility." This may be adequate for systems which own their own transmission. In many cases, however, cooperatives do not own the transmission system used to provide service to their members. Thus, all utilities should be able to recover stranded costs, whether or not they own or control transmission systems.

In addition, when a distribution system loses a customer, its G&T, which has incurred costs to provide power to the distribution system for that customer, is likely to incur a substantial amount of stranded cost as well. FERC's present proposals do not provide a mechanism for the G&T to recover its costs.

Finally, there is the issue of stranded benefits. Some utilities with lower cost power sources could profit by a shift to market pricing. If the argument can be made that a utility losing a load it expected to serve experiences stranded costs, it can also be made that a wholesale customer, such as an electric cooperative, had an expectation that it would continue to be able to purchase power at an attractive rate. If the competitive price exceeds that rate, then the customer experiences stranded benefits. The mega-NOPR does not address this issue.

The mega-NOPR also attempts to define which facilities will be termed transmission and thus fall under its jurisdiction, as opposed to distribution facilities which fell under the state jurisdiction. The proposal says any facility used to deliver power in interstate commerce to a wholesale purchaser is subject to the commission's jurisdiction. If a utility delivers electricity in interstate commerce to an end-user for a third-party supplier, which could be considered a retail wheeling transaction, FERC will determine its jurisdiction on a case-by-case basis, based on factors related to the use of the facilities used to deliver the power. For example, if Virginia Power delivered electricity purchased from Old Dominion Electric Cooperative to a pulp and paper mill in North Carolina, the Commission would examine the details of the transaction to determine which elements constituted interstate transmission, an activity under its jurisdiction, and which constituted a retail sale of generation, which would be subject to state regulation.

Finally, the commission proposes the creation of a real-time information network (RIN) system to provide information on the transmission services available under open access tariffs.

Comments from interested parties on the mega-NOPR were to be submitted to FERC August 1995. The proposed rule is quite detailed, and many issues remain to be sorted out, including such things as what will happen to existing contracts, how capacity will be allocated when it is inadequate to meet everyone's needs, and how resulting changes, such as a wave of mergers, will affect utilities' market power. FERC was expected to issue a final rule in the matter in the first quarter of 1996. The decision will undoubtedly be appealed on various grounds.

Cooperatives that borrow from RUS, including most G&Ts, are not subject to FERC jurisdiction. However, EPAct allows cooperatives to ask FERC to order a transmitting utility to provide transmission service. In return, cooperatives must agree to provide similar wholesale transmission access if so ordered by FERC.

While this would not affect most systems, it raises a number of questions about how the new rules would apply to cooperatives in practice, including concerns about fair pricing for cooperative transmission services, the possibility that revenues from FERC-ordered transmission could push non-member income above fifteen percent and thus make the cooperative subject to income tax, and jeopardize the cooperative's eligibility for RUS financing.

Pricing, Reliability, and the Obligation to Serve
The development of a competitive electricity generation market has come about through legislative and regulatory change. At the same time, it has raised concerns related to pricing and quality of service. One question is whether independent power will be as reliable and efficient as that of traditional suppliers. Experience so far suggests that nonutility generation is just as reliable in operation as conventional sources of power. But this does not necessarily mean that independent power, if it becomes the dominant means of supplying our future capacity needs, will maintain overall system reliability or avoid the inherent risks associated with capital-intensive projects.

Two of the most important aspects of the reliability issue are the financial reliability of the developer and the operational reliability of the project. Critics of competitive generation fear that, since current bidding systems award contracts before projects are actually financed, many projects may fail to be built because the contracts are too competitive (i.e., priced too low) to obtain financing. There is also a fear that some bidding systems give too much weight to price at the expense of the bidders' other capabilities. The bidder that submits the lowest cost project does not necessarily have the greatest ability to complete the project on time and to operate it in a safe and reliable manner.

Conversely, IPPs and other proponents of contract power argue that it is more reliable than utility generation, since profits from such projects are directly related to performance and because operators are penalized (depending on the terms of the contract) for failure to perform as specified. Thus, supporters argue, contract power creates a greater incentive for reliable operation than cost-of-service pricing (which, they contend, only rewards investment, not performance), and actually insulates ratepayers against construction cost overruns, downtime, or project failure. Independents also say the utility's obligation to serve exists only at the retail sales level, and that reliability has not suffered as utilities have increasingly relied on nonutility suppliers.

Cooperatives that consider purchasing from independent power producers will consider a variety of issues. One is the question of who will bear the risk associated with the construction of an IPP project. For example, a great deal of uncertainty remains over the cooperative's liability if IPP power fails to come on line, leaving the cooperative with a capacity shortfall.

IPP contracts may be subject to supply and price fluctuations, changing environmental or safety standards, or new supply or demand-side technology rendering some generation facilities obsolete. While some contracts may insulate against some risks, the IPP's lenders will continue to require a high degree of certainty that such investments will be secure and that the risks will be adequately rewarded. The IPPs purpose is to earn a profit and the greater the level of risk it accepts, the higher the profit it expects. This is a different objective over a cooperative's goal of providing power at the lowest possible cost.

Of course, many of these same risks exist when a distribution system purchases power from a G&T through a wholesale power contract, but there is a strong history behind that relationship and substantial support exists within the rural electric program for cutting the risks and resolving problems. Potential benefits may await some distribution systems and G&Ts that buy from independent sources, but the allocation of risk associated with generation facilities continues to require careful co-op consideration.

The extent to which cooperatives win or lose in the transition to competitive power will depend on their particular needs, the timing and extent of new capacity needs, and whether the regulatory process can adapt to the new environment. If, as a result of competitive pressures, a cooperative's revenues are inadequate to meet its cash expenses, it may be unable to meet its obligations to lenders.

In recent years there have been a number of situations involving both distribution and G&T cooperatives where the co-op was unable to pay its debts. What happens as a result depends on the level of shortfall, the value of the cooperative's assets, and the competitive environment, among other factors. In some cases, the lenders have agreed to restructure the debt. In the most extreme case, a G&T cooperative's assets were sold to other utilities, the cooperative was dissolved, and its member systems entered into power contracts with other suppliers. In that case, the lenders were paid in full. However, it is possible that other troubled situations which have not yet been resolved or that develop in the future will result in significant losses to lenders. If that occurs, some lenders may be less willing to provide financing to cooperatives. Obviously, it is also possible that some cooperative systems will not survive the transition to the competitive market.

Strategies for Competing

Electric cooperatives, like other types of utilities, face increased business and financial risks as a result of the changes taking place in the industry. A report by Moody's Investors Service in mid-1995 predicted an overall decline in credit quality among G&T cooperatives over the next five to 10 years, a factor that would also affect the G&T's member systems. Moody's makes a similar prediction for the investor-owned segment of the industry. There will be winners and losers among cooperatives in the new environment just as there will be for municipal, investor-owned, and independent systems. The winners will be those that offer quality service and competitive rates and, perhaps most important, are able to communicate to their members the value of these services.

A major factor for any cooperative distribution system is its cost of power. In 1994, G&T revenues per kilowatt-hour from sales to member systems ranged from 26.07 to 68.02 mills per kilowatt-hour, and some of the systems with higher rates were not recovering all their costs. In other words, some G&Ts offer very competitive rates, and others don't.

The stranded investment issue for cooperatives is that some G&T systems have invested in more capacity than they can economically use or capacity that is higher in cost than is competitive in today's market. Either way, in order to recover all of its costs, the G&T would have to charge rates that could make its member systems uncompetitive.

Moody's estimates that the 10-year average price for capacity in a purely competitive market will range from $20 to $45 per kilowatt-year, depending on location. At a 15 percent carrying charge typical of an investor-owned utility, that is roughly equivalent to recovering an investment of $133 to $300 per kilowatt. Depending on a unit's energy cost relative to the market price for energy, a system may be able to earn additional margins on energy sales. In 1994, the G&T systems, excluding those involved in debt restructure, bankruptcy, or workouts, had an average total investment of $781 per kilowatt. Although these numbers may not be exactly comparable, they do illustrate the point that the G&Ts, like their counterparts in other segments of the industry, will be facing significant competitive pressures in the next few years.

Because so much of their capacity was installed in the 1970s and 1980s, some G&Ts have invested more per kilowatt on average than their likely competitors. A major challenge under the new industry structure will be finding ways to overcome this basic price disadvantage.

Unfortunately, few options are available for achieving major cost reductions. Taxes are largely beyond the co-op's control. Some systems have been able to reduce interest expense by refinancing higher cost debt. In some cases it is possible to

WITHDRAWAL FROM TVA

If Four County Electric Power Association in Mississippi has its way, they will be the first utility to ever withdraw from the Tennessee Valley Authority. TVA, however, is fighting the attempt, saying that the termination of the power supply contract would cost it millions of dollars a year.

Earl Weeks, Four County general manager, has stated that the co-op is determined to provide the lowest cost, most reliable service to its 37,000 members and that is the driving force behind the withdrawal.

A report done for the co-op indicated that Four County could save $50 million to $70 million over the next ten years by shopping around for other sources of power.

renegotiate fuel or power purchase agreements, or to reduce other operation and maintenance or administrative and general expenses. Reducing these costs, however, is not likely to compensate for high-cost generation investments that can't compete in today's climate.

Obviously, this situation can create conflicts between G&Ts and their member systems. The all-requirements contract is a major advantage for G&T systems, but it loses its appeal for distribution members facing their own competitive pressures. The solution to this problem has yet to emerge, but it is causing some G&Ts to rethink their relationship with their member systems.

Such rethinking is under way in Georgia, where Oglethorpe Power G&T announced in the fall of 1995 that six of its 39 member systems were withdrawing from all-requirements contracts that weren't due to expire for another 30 years. The revamped relationship allows withdrawing systems to shop around for wholesale supplies to meet new demand and to buy from any source, including Oglethorpe. They must continue to use Oglethorpe power for power requirements existing at the time of their withdrawal, to keep the original system whole and avoid hurting other member systems that remain with in the G&T. The new arrangement also allows member systems to use Oglethorpe as a buying agent for outside sources, and permits member systems to install dispersed generating facilities.

The Oglethorpe option may spread to other G&Ts, or power-supply cooperatives may find other ways to meet the competition. G&Ts may form pools with other buyers and sellers to broaden the market for their capacity, or they may be able to work with marketers or brokers to increase sales. They may seek merger partners, or choose to sell some of its assets. To be viable in the future, the G&T and its member systems must cooperate in developing a plan that will meet their respective needs.

Distribution Strategies

David W. Penn, writing in the January-February 1995 issue of *Public Power*, estimated that one-third of the nation's investor-owned utilities were involved in merger negotiations. Cooperatives are also beginning to recognize the financial and operating benefits of consolidation or merger, and more than thirty co-op mergers have taken place since 1980.

In a **consolidation**, two or more systems join by dissolving the original corporations and forming a new one. In a merger, one system is absorbed into the other. A consolidation reflects a joining of equals and is usually preferred for that reason.

MERGERS AND CONSOLIDATIONS REQUIRE PLANNING

Systems considering merger or consolidation can improve their chances for success by developing an action plan to guide their efforts. While the plan should reflect the specific needs of the cooperatives involved, in most cases the following general steps will be included.

1. Each board should hold its own meetings to discuss the merger or consolidation proposal and determine a time frame for the first joint meeting with the other board(s).

2. Each board should be willing to commit manpower and funds to the effort and make that level of commitment known to management.

3. In the first joint meeting, systems should review past actions, common needs and problems, reach agreement about the merger/consolidation study, establish study areas, appoint personnel to study areas and committees, and set the tentative timetable. They should also elect a chair.

4. The directors should meet as a combined board to review progress and discuss problems as they arise.

5. Each board should review the progress at their regular meetings.

6. The boards should develop, as soon as possible, member, public, and employee information programs; review legal steps; and contact and begin work with regulatory agencies, RUS, and supplemental lenders.

7. All work should be aimed at determining the new system's identity, staff, location, and methods of gaining member support and a positive vote by membership (if desirable or required).

8. The combined board oversees the final steps and establishes an effective date for the merger or consolidation.

—*Adapted from* Procedures Manual on Effecting a Merger or Consolidation
National Rural Utilities Cooperative Finance Corporation

Smaller cooperative systems in particular have been able to improve their financial health and reduce costs through mergers, which can dramatically cut payroll and other expenses, and, in many cases, also improve service.

Other systems have been able to gain some of the benefits of merger through shared service contracts or other forms of federation that enable systems to act jointly in some areas while retaining local control of other activities. For example, five cooperative systems in Wisconsin have established a program of joint purchasing, business processing, and contracting.

Another group of cooperatives in Indiana are jointly sponsoring a statewide marketing program aimed at protecting themselves against hostile takeovers. They are so satisfied with the results that they are looking at other areas for cooperation including purchasing and environmental compliance.

While systems should be able to obtain equal benefits through **federation** or consolidation, there is a practical limit to the value of federation. Federated co-ops require two or more boards to agree on all major decisions, which can be difficult to achieve.

Consolidation may produce more lasting and long-term benefits. On the other hand, federation enables the systems to maintain their individual identities, which can be a competitive advantage for co-ops with strong member support.

The Role of Acquisitions

Some cooperatives are finding that acquiring other systems can help them become more efficient and provide benefits to a neighboring utility as well. CFC Senior Vice President for Strategic Services David J. Hedberg estimates that as many as fifty acquisitions are under co-op consideration.

A typical cooperative distribution system territory surrounds a few towns served by investor-owned or municipal utilities. If the co-op can acquire service to the towns, it can substantially increase its load without increasing its boundaries. It may be able to serve and maintain the area with little additional expense.

The changes taking place in the electric utility industry can make this attractive to the potential seller. Small towns typically have a density of 10 to 12 consumers per mile of line. That is quite low by investor-owned or municipal standards but very attractive from a cooperative point of view. In addition, many investor-owned utilities are consolidating their district offices and service centers, making it more difficult and costly to serve outlying areas. With the cost of service regulation being abandoned in many states, the investor-owned companies will no longer be able to increase earnings by investing in more plant. Selling marginal territories may provide a way for them to become more efficient and increase profits. The cooperative may increase the attractiveness of its proposal by agreeing to purchase wholesale power for a time, an arrangement which must be coordinated with any G&T involved.

For an acquisition to work, the consumers of both utilities must also receive benefits. Presumably takeover will result in savings or the acquisition would not be taking place. These savings must be shared by both groups. At a minimum, customers of the acquired system must not see a rate increase; a decrease is preferable. Existing cooperative members must also see a benefit, particularly if their rates have been higher.

Such transactions were seldom contemplated in the past, but they are likely to be increasingly attractive in the future. Acquisition can be a powerful tool in increasing the competitiveness and viability of cooperative systems.

Facing the Future

Electric cooperatives were begun as a means to improve the lives of people in rural areas. Some systems are finding new ways to do that and to provide value-added services to their members by offering telecommunications, water and waste water, economic development, and other services to their member systems.

Competition is here. It requires cooperative management and members to think in new ways. They must evaluate both themselves and their competitors not in terms of how they would like things to be but how they are and potentially will be a year or two in the future.

It is easy to identify some of the weaknesses of cooperative systems. Historically, they have served the least attractive service territories. Their traditional source of financing, RUS, is changing in many ways and experiencing the pressures all government agencies are experiencing. Taken by themselves, most cooperatives are small organizations lacking the resources of major investor-owned utilities and independent power producers.

But cooperatives also enjoy tremendous strengths. Collectively, in 1994, they had more than $60 billion in assets. They have built a strong support system in the G&Ts, the statewide organizations, and national organizations such as NRECA and CFC. RUS has encouraged uniform—and thus lower cost—materials, as well as common accounting system and engineering standards. These factors have fostered a unity and cohesiveness among systems that encourages cooperation to meet mutual goals. Finally, perhaps the most important—if also the most fragile—asset is the support of 30 million member-owners. That support must be nourished with competitive rates and superior service as cooperatives prepare to compete in a new electric utility industry.

CO-OP ACQUISITION OF IOU BENEFITS EVERYONE

Tri-County Rural Electric Cooperative, Inc. serves 16,500 mostly residential members over 3,000 miles of line in a 5,000 square mile service territory at the northern edge of Pennsylvania. Wellsboro Electric Company (WECo), a for-profit investor-owned utility, serves 5,200 consumers over 525 miles of line in a 180 square mile service territory located in the middle of Tri-County's service area. On January 4, 1995, they accomplished something that would have been unthinkable only a few years ago. Tri-County acquired 92.6 percent of the outstanding shares of Wellsboro stock through its subsidiary Wilderness Area Utilities, Inc. and entered into a management services agreement to operate its former competitor. The changes taking place in the electric industry made the acquisition attractive to WECo, Tri-County, and the consumers of both utilities.

"WECo's location in the heart of Tri-County's service territory makes an alliance an ideal way to achieve greater economies of scale and neutralize a competitor," said Tri-County manager Robert O. Toombs.

Aside from the difference in corporate structure, Tri-County, as a cooperative, is not subject to regulation by the Pennsylvania Public Utilities Commission. WECo is subject to commission jurisdiction. At the time acquisition negotiations started, Tri-County's basic residential rate was about fifty percent higher than WECo's. Beyond that, the two systems had much in common. They were geographically connected. Both were distribution systems with similar operations, purchasing needs, and staff activities.

Pennsylvania law prohibits cooperatives from serving in incorporated areas of more than 2,500 residents. WECo serves the borough of Wellsboro, population 4,000, so a merger was not legally possible. Tri-County established Wilderness Area Utilities as a wholly-owned, for-profit subsidiary specifically to acquire the WECo stock. The $10 million acquisition was financed by CFC through its associate member program. The transaction required the approval of the Pennsylvania Public Utilities Commission, RUS, and the Securities and Exchange Commission.

In order to make a smooth transition, Tri-County implemented a business plan that addressed five major areas: personnel assimilation, consumer services, wholesale power contracts, engineering and operations, and legal and financial considerations. In many respects, the systems will operate as if a merger had taken place.

In order to minimize potential employee opposition, Tri-County agreed to retain WECo's existing staff. It plans to eliminate duplicative positions and reduce the total number of employees for the two systems by about ten percent over a period of five years through retirements and attrition. The systems share management staff. Tri-County is taking steps to standardize pay scales for both union and non-union employees of the combined organization.

continued on next page

CO-OP ACQUISITION OF IOU BENEFITS EVERYONE
CONTINUED FROM PAGE 167

Prior to the acquisition, WECo did not have a customer service department, a communications program, or a marketing plan. Tri-County has trained a WECo staff member to handle bill complaints and answer energy use questions and is providing support in other member services and communications area. Tri-County offers several special energy efficiency marketing programs, including water heater discounts, off-peak rates for electric thermal storage, and geothermal heat pump rebates, which it hopes to extend to WECo consumers.

Tri-County purchases all of its power requirements from a G&T, Allegheny Electric Cooperative. WECo purchases its power requirements from Pennsylvania Electric Company under an agreement that includes a two-year notice period for termination. While WECo will continue to purchase power under its existing agreement for the time being, the cooperative will explore the possibility of switching WECo to Allegheny in the future.

Many of the benefits of the combination are expected to accrue from increased efficiency in the engineering and operations area. The systems are reducing inventory, coordinating vehicle purchases, retiring duplicative equipment, and participating in joint purchasing through a local co-op purchasing group. Tri-County has also agreed to make badly needed upgrades and repairs to WECo's distribution system and is in the process of developing a long-range engineering plan to modernize the aging system. The upgrades will reduce line loss and improve load factors as well as reliability.

Finally, Tri-County is revamping WECo's accounting and financial planning systems to make them compatible with the cooperative's operations.

The acquisition has enabled Tri-County to take advantage of new economies of scale to reduce costs and has provided new revenue resources. The cooperative has access to a larger work force which has helped to reduce outage times due to storms. The ability to share many resources, such as computers, dispatch, equipment, and management, is expected to reduce costs and improve efficiency. While about 95 percent of Tri-County's members are residential or seasonal, about 15 percent of WECo's consumers are classified as commercial or industrial users, providing a needed diversity to the joint system. WECo's density, about ten consumers per mile of line, is attractive compared to Tri-County's five consumers per mile of line.

Each of the parties to this transaction came out a winner, but perhaps the biggest winners are the consumers. The benefits of the arrangement are expected to stabilize rates for both systems well into the next century. While there was no practical way of standardizing rates across the two systems in the short term, neither experienced a rate increase as a result of the acquisition. The economies of scale and other cost-saving opportunities are expected to reduce the need for increase in the future.

APPENDICES

TABLE OF ACRONYMS

AEP: American Electric Power Company

APA: Alaska Power Association

APPA: American Public Power Association

BC: Bank for Cooperatives

BAT: Best Available Technology

BCT: Best Conventional Technology

BPA: Bonneville Power Administration

BPT: Best Practicable Technology

CFC: National Rural Utilities Cooperative Finance Corporation

CPR: Continuing Property Records

CPUC: California Public Utilities Commission

DOE: Department of Energy

DSC: Debt Service Coverage Ratio

ECAR: East Central Area Reliability Coordination Agreement

EEI: Edison Electric Institute

EIA: Energy Information Administration

EIS: Environmental Impact Statement

EMC: Electric Membership Corporation

EMF: Electromagnetic Fields

EPA: Environmental Protection Agency

EPAct: Energy Policy Act of 1992

ERA: Economic Regulatory Administration

EWG: Exempt Wholesale Generation

FCC: Federal Communications Commission

FERC: Federal Energy Regulatory Commission

FFB: Federal Financing Bank

FPA: Federal Power Act

FPC: Federal Power Commission

FIFO: First-in, First-out

GENCO: Generating Company

G&T: Generation & Transmission System

IOU: Investor-Owned Utility

IPP: Independent Power Producer

IPCC: Intergovernmental Panel on Climate Change

ISO: Independent System Operator

KRTA: Key Ratio Trend Analysis

Kwh: Kilowatt–Hour

LIBOR: London Interbank Offered Rate

MAAC: Mid-Atlantic Area Council

MAIN: Mid-America Interpool Network

MAPP: Mid-Continent Area Power Pool

MWH: Megawatt-Hour

MOU: Memorandum of Understanding

NCSC: National Cooperative Services Corporation

NERC: National Electric Reliability Council

NEPA: National Environmental Policy Act of 1969

NPCC: Northeast Power Coordinating Council

NRECA: National Rural Electric Cooperative Association

NRTC: National Rural Telecommunications Cooperative

NGPA: Natural Gas Policy Act of 1978

NOPR: Notice of Proposed Rulemaking

NRC: Nuclear Regulatory Commission

NUG: Nonutility Generation

ODSC: Operating Debt Service Coverage Ratio

OTIER: Operating Times Interest Earned Ratio

PMA: Power Marketing Administration

PRR: Plant Revenue Ratio

PURPA: Public Utility Regulatory Policies Act of 1978

PUHCA: Public Utility Holding Company Act

QF: Qualifying Facility

RCRA: Resource Conservation and Recovery Act

REA: Rural Electrification Administration

RELRA: Rural Electrification Loan Restructuring Act of 1993

RIN: Real-time Information Network

RTB: Rural Telephone Bank

RTFC: Rural Telephone Financing Cooperative

RTG: Regional Transmission Group

RUS: Rural Utilities Service

SEC: Securities and Exchange Commission

SEPA: Southeastern Power Administration

SERC: Southeastern Electric Reliability Council

SIP: State Implementation Plan

SPP: Small Power Producer

SWPA: Southwestern Power Administration

TIER: Times Interest Earned Ratio

TOU: Time of Use

TVA: Tennessee Valley Authority

WAPA: Western Area Power Administration

WSCC: Western Systems Coordinating Council

GLOSSARY OF TERMS

affiliated companies: companies, one of which owns a controlling or influential share of the other(s), which are controlled by the same parent company.

ampere: the measure of the rate of flow of electrons past a given point in an electric conductor such as a power line; the unit of measurement of electric current, analogous to cubic feet of water flowing per second.

area coverage: one of the basic principles guiding the development of the rural electric programs, area coverage is achieved when all consumers in a co-op's service areas are either served or have service available without extra charges for the construction of facilities and when there are no unserved communities or areas outside the co-op's present service area that it might be expected to serve.

avoided cost: the incremental cost to an electric utility of energy or capacity which, but for the purchase of such power from a QF, the utility would generate itself or purchase from another source.

balance sheet: accounting records showing at any one time the assets, liabilities, and net worth of a business.

Bank for Cooperatives (BC): part of the Farm Credit system, the Farm Credit Act of 1933 created thirteen BCs to finance rural electric and telephone cooperatives. In 1989, eleven of the BCs consolidated to form the National Bank for Cooperatives—CoBank.

base load: the nearly steady level of demand on a utility system; the minimum continuous load or demand in a power system over a given period of time.

base load plant: a plant which is normally operated to take all or part of the minimum continuous load of an electric system and which consequently produces electricity at a constant rate.

bond: a certificate bearing a promise to pay interest and repay principal of borrowed funds.

brokers: parties who arrange transactions between buyers and sellers of electricity and earn commissions on the deal; the broker does not take title to the power and is not subject to FERC regulation.

capacity: the power output rating of a generator or electric system, typically reported in megawatts.

capital intensive: requiring proportionally greater investment in facilities and access to credit in order to produce and deliver service.

capital credits: also called patronage capital, any net margin of revenue over expenses that is credited to cooperative members in proportion to their use of electricity.

capital structure: the proportion of stocks and bonds represented in the capitalization of a corporation.

capitalism: an economic system in which individuals are free to earn profit using the land, labor, and capital available to them.

capitalization: the amount of the face or stated value of the securities issued by a corporation.

central station electric service: electricity produced by large generating plants, usually greater than 350 megawatts, which is delivered via the transmission grid.

cogeneration: joint production of electricity and useful heat from a common source.

combined-cycle plant: the combination of one or more gas turbine and steam turbines in a generating plant; electricity is produced from waste heat from one or more gas turbines. The waste heat is routed to a boiler or to a heat recovery steam generator for use by a steam turbine in the production of electricity.

commercial paper: a form of short-term unsecured debt that has a specific maturity (usually from one to 270 days), represented by a promissory note, or contract between borrower and lender.

competition: freedom of economic choice in buying, selling, or exchanging goods and services.

conductors: materials which allow their electrons to be easily transferred.

consolidation: a joining of equals, when two or more systems join by dissolving the original corporations to form a new one.

cooperative: a non-profit utility owned by its members.

cost of service: the total cost, including operation, maintenance, and administrative costs, taxes, and depreciation expense, to produce electric service.

cost of service study: a study designed to determine the cost of providing service to various classes of customers, which is used as a basis for establishing rates.

current assets: property and property rights which are used in present operations of a business, such as cash inventory, and the like.

debenture bonds: a bond backed by the general credit of the company but without a specific pledge of property by mortgage or other collateral.

demand: the rate at which electric energy is delivered to customers by a system at a given instant—or averaged over a designated period—usually expressed in kilowatts or megawatts.

demand charge: the portion of electric rates which is expected to recover the costs associated with the level of demand for service. Included in demand charges are capital or investment related costs and the cost of operation and maintenance of generation, transmission and distribution.

demand side management: activities or programs undertaken by a utility or its customers to influence the amount and timing of electricity consumption.

depreciation: the wearing out or loss of service value of property used in business operations.

dispersed generation: small generating units that may be placed throughout a power supply system rather than at a central location.

distribution: actual delivery of electricity to the end user.

distribution systems: the system of lines, transformers and switches that connect between the transmission network and customer load; that portion of an electric utility system that delivers service directly to the end user at relatively low voltages. Most electric cooperatives are distribution systems, purchasing generation and transmission services from other organizations. Most investor-owned electric utilities own generation, transmission and distribution assets.

easement: the purchase of the right to use land for a limited purpose and time with another person retaining ownership.

elasticity of demand: the degree to which demand will vary with a change in price.

electricity: the motion of electrons through a conductor.

embedded cost: an historical cost, or a cost that was incurred in the past; the historical cost of all facilities in the power supply system.

eminent domain: the authority whereby land may be taken from a private owner in order to permit use by the public.

empowerment: providing employees with the resources needed to achieve their goals.

energy export taxes: state taxes imposed on utilities that export energy to consumers in another state.

energy charge: the commodity charge, or the portion of the charge for electric service that is based on the electric energy (Kwh) consumed or billed.

equity capital: ownership investment in a corporation evidenced by common (voting) and preferred (sometimes nonvoting) stocks; the sum of capital from retained earnings and the issuance of stock.

excise taxes: taxes imposed on the manufacture, sale, or consumption of commodities and services.

exempt wholesale generators (EWGs): independent power producers who generate power and sell it on a wholesale basis and who are exempt from the restrictions imposed by the Public Utility Holding Company Act.

FERC: the Federal Energy Regulatory Commission is a part of the U.S. Department of Energy and is the key utility regulatory agency of the federal government.

FIFO method: one method of returning margins to cooperative members, the "first-in, first-out" method returns oldest investments first without regard to the level of investment.

fixed assets: assets represented by plant and equipment.

fixed costs: those expenses of a business enterprise which do not vary in relation to changes in volume of output, such as interest on borrowed funds, insurance, or general overhead expenses.

franchise taxes: local taxes imposed for the privilege of providing utility service within city limits.

functional unbundling: a proposal by FERC to implement full open access of the electric transmission system through the separation of the transmission, distribution, and generation functions of utilities. Under the proposal, a utility must obtain transmission service for all of its new wholesale sales and purchases under the same tariff it applies when offering these services to others—the tariff must include separate rates for transmission and ancillary services.

functionalize: to allocate costs of providing electric service according to the generation, transmission, or distribution functions.

gas turbine: a compressor which feeds compressed air into one or more combustion chambers where liquid or gaseous fuel is burned. The resulting hot gases are expanded through the turbine, causing it to rotate. The rotating turbine shaft drives the compressors as well as the generator, producing electricity.

generation: the actual production of electricity.

generation and transmission cooperatives (G&Ts): cooperative organizations that own power plants, generate electricity and transmit it at wholesale to distribution cooperatives. Some G&Ts also have distribution systems for delivery of power to end users.

greenhouse effect: solar radiation absorbed by the earth, converted to heat, and trapped close to the earth's surface by water vapor and gases such as CO_2.

grid: the layout of the electrical transmission system or a synchronized transmission network.

hardship loans: loans available from RUS to systems whose residential rate exceeds 15 cents per Kwh and those systems that have residential rates exceeding 120 percent of their state average and serve consumers whose income is below their state average; the loans carry an interest rate of five percent and recipients are not required to obtain supplemental financing.

holding company: an organization not directly engaged in the operation of any business, but which owns the stock of other companies.

income method: a method of valuing a cooperative's property that calculates the value based on the income it generates.

incremental costs: extra expenses incurred from the production of an additional quantity of service.

independent power producer (IPP): a nonutility power generating entity, defined by the 1978 Public Utility Regulatory Policies Act, that sells power it generates to electric utilities at wholesale prices.

interconnection: a tie line or connection permitting the flow of electric energy between the facilities of two electric systems.

intermediate load: the range from base load to a point between base and peak loads.

investor-owned utilities (IOU): a utility company organized under state law as a publicly traded corporation for the purpose of providing utility service and earning a profit for its stockholders.

kilowatt-hour (Kwh): a measure of electricity consumption equivalent to the use of one thousand watts of power over a one-hour period.

kilowatt (Kw): a measure of electric power equal to one thousand watts.

leveraged lease: a financing technique whereby a utility sells an asset to a second party who finances the purchase primarily through the issuance of debt and who leases the asset back to the utility for operation.

liability: an obligation due to another; an amount payable in dollars or by future services to be rendered.

margin: the difference between net sales and the cost of providing service.

marginal cost: the incremental cost of serving any additional demand, volume, or customers over or beyond a previous pattern or level of consumption.

marginal cost pricing: a system of pricing designed to ignore all costs except those associated with producing the next increment of power generation; also referred to as incremental cost pricing.

market value: the price at which stock is presently selling on the stock market.

medium-term notes: unsecured obligations with a longer term to maturity than commercial paper, ranging from 271 days up to 30 years.

megawatt (MW): a unit of electrical power equal to one million watts or one thousand kilowatts.

money desk: a structure within the National Rural Utilities Cooperative Finance Corporation which issues commercial paper and medium-term notes directly to members and other qualified investors.

monopoly: absence of competition in any economic relationship.

mortgage bonds: bonds offering security for repayment in the form of a mortgage on the company's property or some specified part thereof.

municipal utility: a utility owned and operated by a municipality or group of municipalities.

natural monopoly: an activity such as the provision of gas, water, and electrical service characterized by economies of scale wherein cost of service is minimized if a single enterprise is the only seller in the market.

net margins: revenues a cooperative collects in excess of operating costs, net margins are treated as equity capital and must eventually be returned to members.

nonutility generator: facility for generating electricity that is not exclusively or primarily owned by an electric utility and which operates connected to an electric utility system.

occupational taxes: taxes imposed on businesses in return for the privilege of doing business locally.

ohm: the unit of measurement of electrical resistance; the resistance of a circuit in which a potential difference of one volt produces a current of one ampere.

original cost: as a measure of fair value, this is the amount of investment made to build or buy a given plant when first devoted to public service.

parent company: owns the stock of one or more subsidiaries and may be a holding company.

patronage capital: any revenues in excess of operating costs which are treated as equity capital contributed by the cooperative's members, and which eventually must be returned to the members in proportion to their purchase of electricity.

peak demand: the maximum load during a specified amount of time.

peaking capacity: the capacity of generating equipment that is used to meet the highest daily, weekly, or seasonal loads—short periods when consumers use much more power.

percentage method: one method of returning margins to cooperative members, this method returns capital in accordance with a percentage of the total amount of capital credits on the cooperative's books and the member's total contribution to the capital credits.

postage stamp rate: a rate for electricity that does not vary according to distance from the power supply.

power marketer: parties that purchase bulk power for resale at market rates; marketers take title to the power and become subject to FERC regulation.

power marketing administrations (PMAs): Congress established five federal power marketing administrations to sell hydroelectric power generated by federal dams and power plants: Bonneville Power Administration, Western Area Power Administration, Southwestern Power Administration, Southeastern Power Administration, and Alaska Power Administration.

power pools: an association of two or more electric systems interconnected for the sharing of reserve generating capacity and power production coordination.

preference: a provision written in law that gives publicly owned utilities and cooperatives priority access to federal power.

price cap: a method of setting a utility distribution company's rates whereby a maximum allowable price is established by regulators, flexibility in pricing is allowed, and efficiency gains can be captured by the company.

property taxes: taxes imposed at the local level based on the value of real estate, personal property, or intangible property.

public utility: a business enterprise rendering a service considered essential to the public and, as such, subject to regulation in the public interest, usually by statutory law.

pumped storage hydroelectric plant: a plant that produces power from water that had previously been pumped to an upper reservoir.

PURPA: the Public Utility Regulatory Policies Act of 1978 requires utilities to provide open access to transmission lines, for use by independent power producers and nonutility generators and requires utilities to purchase excess power produced by cogeneration facilities.

purchased power adjustment: a clause in a rate schedule that provides for adjustments to the bill when energy purchased from another electric system is acquired and it varies from a specified price.

qualifying facility (QF): any nonutility generation plant that qualifies under the specifications of PURPA to sell power to public utilities.

rate base: the value of property upon which an investor-owned utility is given the opportunity to earn a specified rate of return as established by a regulatory authority. The rate base represents the value of property used by the utility in providing service.

rate design: the development of electricity prices for various customer classes to meet revenue requirements determined by operating needs and costs.

rate of return: the profit that a regulated investor-owned utility is given the opportunity to earn.

rating: ratings assigned by independent rating agencies representing an assessment of the borrower's ability to repay principal and interest.

regional transmission group: voluntary organization of transmission system owners, wholesale purchasers, and independent power producers interested in coordinating wholesale wheeling.

reliability: the degree to which an electric utility delivers service to customers within accepted standards and in the amount desired. The degree of reliability may be measured by the frequency, duration, and magnitude of adverse affects on service to the customer.

reproduction cost: as a measure of fair value, is the amount which would be required to build a given plant today.

reserves: the electric power needed to provide service to customers in the event of generation or transmission outages, or other factors that may restrict generating capability or increase loads.

retail: sales of electric energy supplied for residential, commercial and industrial end use purposes; other classes such as agriculture and street lighting are included in this category.

retail wheeling: the sale of electricity by a utility or other supplier to a customer in another utility's retail service territory. Wheeling refers to the use of the local utility's transmission and distribution lines to deliver the power from a wholesale supplier to a retail customer by a third party.

revenue: the funds a utility must take in to cover the sum of its estimated operation and maintenance expenses, debt service, and taxes.

revenue bonds: bonds upon which the company promises to pay interest, secured by the company's earnings ability.

revenue requirement: the amount an investor-owned utility must collect to pay expenses and provide a fair return to investors.

revenue taxes: taxes imposed on business gross receipts or otherwise based on revenue, sometimes in place of, or in addition to, property taxes.

RIN: Real-time Information Network. A method proposed by FERC to have information available via electronic bulletin board about transmission availability, scheduling, economic dispatch and service interruptions.

Rural Electrification Administration (REA): created in 1935 under the authority of the Emergency Relief Appropriation Act of 1935, REA was established as an independent lending agency with the passage of the Rural Electrification Act of 1936; REA's goal was to electrify rural America.

Rural Utilities Service (RUS): a new federal agency created in 1994 to succeed the Rural Electrification Administration which was abolished by a reorganization of the Department of Agriculture.

sales for resale: energy supplied to other electric utilities, cooperatives, municipalities, and Federal and state agencies for resale to ultimate consumers; wholesale sales.

sinking fund: funds set aside annually which, with growth, will be used for repayment of principal on bonds or to replace retired property.

small power producer (SPP): a facility that generates electricity using waste, renewable (water, wind and solar), or geothermal energy as a primary energy resource—and although fossil fuels can be used, renewable resources must provide at least seventy-five percent of total energy.

stranded costs/investment: an investment with a cost recovery schedule that was initially approved by regulatory action that subsequent regulatory action or market forces has rendered not practically recoverable; costs that electric utilities are currently permitted to recover through rates but whose recovery may be prevented by the advent of competition in the industry.

subsidiary: a company whose stock is owned by a controlling organization.

tax-exempt financing: bonds issued to finance pollution control facilities in the early 1980s which did not require the bondholder to pay state or federal income taxes on the interest earnings of the bond.

territorial protection: the cooperative's desire to maintain electric service to rural areas that developed into attractive service territories.

test period: an historic period of time selected and used as a proxy for the future in the rate-setting process.

transformer: an electrical device for changing the voltage of alternating current.

transmission: the network of high voltage lines, transformers, and switches used to move electrical power from generators to the distribution system; also used to interconnect different utility systems and independent power producers together into a synchronized network.

unbundled services: the selling and pricing of services separately as opposed to offering services "bundled" into packages with a single price for the whole package.

valuation: the assigning of values to the properties of a utility enterprise to establish fair value for rate making or other purposes.

variable costs: those expenses of a business enterprise which vary with changes in volume of output, such as outlays for fuel to generate electric power.

volt: the unit of electromotive force or electric pressure analogous to water pressure in pounds per square inch.

watt: the electrical unit of power or rate of doing work; the rate of energy transfer equivalent to one ampere flowing under a pressure of one volt at unity power factor.

wheeling: an electric utility operation wherein transmission facilities of one system are used to transmit power produced by another system.

wholesale sales: energy supplied to other electric utilities, cooperatives, municipal, Federal and state electric agencies, as well as power marketers for resale to ultimate consumers.

working capital: the amount of cash required to operate a utility during the interim between the rendering of service and receipt of payment.

LIST OF COOPERATIVES

ALABAMA

Name of Cooperative	Type*	Consumer Members	Phone Number
Alabama Electric Co-op, Inc.	GT		(334) 222-2571
Alabama Rural Electric Assn.	S		(205) 215-2732
Arab Electric Cooperative, Inc.	D	12,424	(205) 586-3196
Baldwin County EMC	D	31,422	(205) 989-6247
Black Warrior EMC	O	23,002	(205) 289-0845
Central Alabama Electric Co-op	D	26,218	(205) 365-6762
Cherokee Electric Co-op	D	17,668	(205) 927-5524
Clarke-Washington EMC	D	16,931	(205) 246-9081
Coosa Valley Electric Co-op Inc.	D	11,193	(205) 362-4180
Covington Electric Co-op	D	18,977	(205) 222-4121
Cullman Electric Cooperative	D	32,870	(205) 737-3240
Dixie Electric Co-op	D	11,599	(205) 738-2500
Franklin Electric Co-op, Inc.	D	6,898	(205) 332-2730
Joe Wheeler EMC	D	34,644	(205) 351-6517
Marshall DeKalb Electric Co-op	D	14,940	(205) 593-4262
North Alabama Electric Co-op	D	15,337	(205) 437-2281
Pea River Electric Co-op	D	15,068	(205) 774-2545
Pioneer Electric Cooperative	D	12,530	(205) 382-6636
Sand Mountain Electric Co-op	D	24,668	(205) 638-2153
South Alabama Electric Co-op	D	12,818	(334) 566-2060
Southern Pine Electric Co-op	D	17,159	(205) 867-5415
Tallapoosa River Electric Co-op	D	17,201	(205) 864-9331
Tombigbee Electric Co-op, Inc.	D	8,890	(205) 468-3325
Wiregrass Electric Co-op, Inc.	D	14,599	(334) 588-2223

*See page 226 for Key

ALASKA

Name of Cooperative	Type*	Consumer Members	Phone Number
Alaska Electric G&T, Inc.	GT		(907) 235-8167
Alaska Rural Electric Co-op Assn.	S		(907) 561-6103
Alaska Village Electric Co-op, Inc.	D	5,584	(907) 561-1818
Barrow Utilities & Electric Co-op	D	15,000	(907) 852-6166
Chugach Electric Assn., Inc.	D	62,535	(907) 563-7494
Cooper Valley Electric Assn., Inc.	D	2,908	(907) 822-3211
Cordova Electric Cooperative	D	1,565	(907) 424-5555
Golden Valley Electric Assn., Inc.	D	27,070	(907) 452-1151
Homer Electric Assn., Inc.	D	18,886	(907) 235-8167
I-N-N Electric Cooperative, Inc.	D	247	(907) 571-1285
Kodiak Electric Assn., Inc.	D	5,301	(907) 486-7700
Kotzebue Electric Assn., Inc.	D	1,023	(907) 442-3491
Mantanuska Electric Assn., Inc.	D	30,542	(907) 745-3231
Metlakatla Power & Light	O	694	(907) 886-4451
Naknek Electric Assn., Inc.	D	764	(907) 246-4261
Nushagak Electric Co-op, Inc.	D	1,161	(907) 842-5251
Tlingit-Haida Electrical Authority	D	1,266	(907) 789-3196
Unalakleet Valley Electric Co-op	D	316	(907) 624-3474
Yakutat Power, Inc.	D	330	(907) 784-3248

ARIZONA

Name of Cooperative	Type*	Consumer Members	Phone Number
Arizona Electric Power Co-op, Inc.	GT		(602) 586-3631
Central Arizona Irrigation Dist.	O		(602) 466-7336
Duncan Valley Electric Co-op, Inc.	D	1,899	(602) 359-2503
Electrical District #2	D	2,586	(520) 723-7741
Electrical District #4	D	375	(602) 466-7336
Electrical District #5	D	292	(602) 682-3442
Graham County Electric Co-op, Inc.	D	6,325	(520) 485-2451
Grand Canyon State Electric Co-op	S		(602) 264-4198

*See page 226 for Key

Name of Cooperative	Type*	Consumer Members	Phone Number
Mohave Electric Co-op, Inc.	D	25,525	(602) 763-4115
Navajo Tribal Utility Authority	D	25,859	(602) 729-5721
Navopache Electric Co-op, Inc.	D	24,567	(602) 368-5118
Sulphur Springs Valley Elec. Co-op	D	32,782	(520) 384-2221
Tohono O'odham Utility Authority	D	2,861	(602) 383-2236
Trico Electric Co-op, Inc.	D	14,854	(602) 744-2944

ARKANSAS

Name of Cooperative	Type*	Consumer Members	Phone Number
Arkansas Electric Co-op Corp.	GT		(501) 570-2200
Arkansas Electric Co-ops, Inc.	S		(501) 570-2200
Arkansas Valley Elec. Co-op Corp.	D	38,534	(501) 667-2176
Ashley-Chicot Electric Co-op, Inc.	D	4,276	(501) 853-5212
C & L Electric Co-op Corp.	D	17,282	(501) 628-4221
Carroll Electric Co-op Corp.	D	49,144	(501) 423-2161
Clay County Electric Co-op Corp.	D	10,766	(501) 857-3661
Craighead Electric Co-op Corp.	D	21,667	(501) 932-8301
Elec. Co-ops Federal Credit Union	O		(501) 570-2396
Farmers Electric Co-op Corp.	D	4,594	(501) 523-3691
First Electric Co-op Corp.	D	54,245	(501) 982-4545
Mississippi County Elec. Co-op	D	3,483	(501) 763-4563
North Arkansas Electric Co-op, Inc.	D	25,051	(501) 895-3221
Ouachita Electric Co-op Corp.	D	8,732	(501) 836-5791
Ozarks Electric Co-op Corp.	D	39,093	(501) 521-2900
Petit Jean Electric Co-op	D	14,746	(501) 745-2493
Rich Mountain Electric Co-op, Inc.	D	6,302	(501) 394-4140
South Central Arkansas Elec. Co-op	D	8,288	(501) 246-6701
Southwest Arkansas Elec. Co-op Corp	D	21,931	(501) 772-2743
Woodruff Electric Co-op Corp.	D	16,163	(501) 633-2262

*See page 226 for Key

CALIFORNIA

Name of Cooperative	Type*	Consumer Members	Phone Number
Anza Electric Co-op, Inc.	D	3,429	(909) 763-4333
California RECA	O		(909) 763-4333
Plumas-Sierra Rural Electric Co-op	D	5,558	(916) 832-4261
Surprise Valley Electrification	D	4,911	(916) 233-3511
Trinity County PUD	D	6,435	(916) 623-5536
Truckee-Donner PUD	D	7,899	(916) 587-3896

COLORADO

Name of Cooperative	Type*	Consumer Members	Phone Number
CoBank-National Bank for Co-ops	O		(303) 740-4000
Colorado REA	S		(303) 455-2700
Delta-Montrose Electric Assn.	D	20,751	(303) 874-8081
Empire Electric Assn., Inc.	D	11,390	(303) 565-4444
Grand Valley Rural Power Lines	D	8,639	(303) 242-0040
Gunnison County Electric Assn.	D	6,184	(303) 641-3520
Highline Electric Association	D	8,697	(303) 854-2236
Holy Cross Electric Assn., Inc.	D	33,963	(303) 945-5491
Intermountain REA	D	57,512	(303) 688-3100
K. C. Electric Association	D	5,890	(719) 743-2431
La Plata Electric Assn., Inc.	D	23,518	(303) 247-5786
Midwest Electric Consumers Assn.	O		(303) 296-2158
Morgan County REA	D	6,124	(970) 867-5688
Mountain Parks Electric, Inc.	D	12,029	(303) 887-3378
Mountain View Electric Assn., Inc.	D	19,109	(719) 775-2861
Poudre Valley REA, Inc.	D	20,987	(303) 226-1234
Rocky Mountain Generation Co-op	GT		(303) 221-1777
Rural Electric Credit Union	O		(303) 695-6354
San Isabel Electric Assn.	D	12,030	(719) 547-2160
San Luis Valley REC, Inc.	D	8,159	(719) 852-3538
San Miguel Power Assn., Inc.	D	7,504	(303) 864-7311

*See page 226 for Key

Name of Cooperative	Type*	Consumer Members	Phone Number
Sangre De Cristo Electric Assn.	D	6,317	(719) 395-2412
Southeast Colorado Power Assn.	D	8,979	(719) 384-2551
United Power, Inc.	D	22,968	(303) 659-0551
Upper Colorado Environmental Plant	O		(303) 878-5003
Western Fuels-Utah, Inc.	O		(303) 675-8431
Western United Electric Supply Corp	O		(303) 455-2725
White River Electric Assn., Inc.	D	2,474	(303) 878-5041
Y. W. Electric Assn., Inc.	D	7,429	(303) 345-2291
Yampa Valley Electric Assn., Inc.	D	18,069	(303) 879-1160

CONNECTICUT

Connecticut Mun. Elec. Energy Co-op	O		(203) 889-4088

DELAWARE

Delaware Electric Co-op, Inc.	D	48,170	(302) 349-4571

DISTRICT OF COLUMBIA

Consumer Energy Council of America	O		(202) 659-0404
Farm Credit Council	O		(202) 626-8710
National Cooperative Bank	O		(202) 336-7700
National Council of Farmer Co-ops	O		(202) 626-8710
Western Fuels Association, Inc.	O		(202) 463-6580

FLORIDA

Central Florida Electric Co-op	D	22,320	(904) 493-2511
Choctawhatchee Electric Co-op, Inc.	D	23,818	(904) 892-2111
Clay Electric Co-op, Inc.	D	107,663	(904) 473-5538
Cooperatives Computer Center	O		(904) 562-0121
Escambia River Electric Co-op, Inc.	O	7,753	(904) 675-4521
Florida Electric Co-op Association	S		(904) 877-6166

*See page 226 for Key

continued on page 192

FLORIDA *(continued)*

Name of Cooperative	Type*	Consumer Members	Phone Number
Florida Keys Electric Co-op Assn.	D	27,956	(305) 852-2431
Florida Municipal Power Agency	O		(407) 859-7310
Glades Electric Co-op, Inc.	D	12,601	(941) 946-0061
Gulf Coast Electric Co-op, Inc.	D	12,965	(904) 639-2216
Lee County Electric Co-op, Inc.	D	126,932	(813) 995-2121
Peace River Electric Co-op, Inc.	D	19,304	(813) 773-4116
Seminole Electric Co-op, Inc.	GT		(813) 963-0994
Sumter ElectricCo-op, Inc.	D	76,707	(904) 793-3801
Suwannee Valley Electric Co-op	D	15,862	(904) 362-2226
Talquin Electric Co-op, Inc.	D	38,830	(904) 627-7651
Tri-County Electric Co-op, Inc.	D	12,749	(904) 973-2285
West Florida Electric Co-op Assn.	D	21,201	(904) 263-3231
Withlacoochee River Electric Co-op	D	131,721	(904) 567-5133

GEORGIA

Name of Cooperative	Type*	Consumer Members	Phone Number
Altamaha EMC	D	14,345	(912) 526-8181
Amicalola EMC	D	23,099	(706) 692-6471
Blue Ridge Mountain EMC	D	27,084	(706) 379-3121
Canoochee EMC	D	13,627	(912) 557-4391
Carroll EMC	D	30,292	(404) 832-3552
Central Georgia EMC	D	25,086	(404) 775-7857
Coastal EMC	D	8,932	(912) 884-3311
Cobb EMC	D	110,868	(404) 429-2100
Colquitt EMC	D	39,283	(912) 985-3620
Coweta-Fayette EMC	D	38,452	(404) 253-5626
Excelsior EMC	D	14,056	(912) 685-2115
Federation/LAF	O		(404) 524-6882
Flint EMC	D	48,803	(912) 847-3415
GEMC Federal Credit Union	O		(404) 270-7851

*See page 226 for Key

Name of Cooperative	Type*	Consumer Members	Phone Number
Georgia EMC	S		(404) 270-6950
Georgia Rural Elec. Service Corp.	O		(912) 847-3421
Grady EMC	D	13,402	(912) 377-4182
GreyStone Power Corporation	D	55,523	(404) 942-6576
Habersham EMC	D	20,620	(706) 754-2114
Hart EMC	D	25,780	(706) 376-4714
Irwin EMC	D	8,944	(921) 468-7654
Jackson EMC	D	100,925	(706) 367-5281
Jefferson EMC	D	25,356	(912) 625-7265
Lamar EMC	D	12,116	(404) 358-1383
Little Ocmulgee EMC	D	8,121	(912) 568-7171
Middle Georgia EMC	D	5,653	(912) 268-2671
Mitchell EMC	D	18,342	(912) 336-5221
North Georgia EMC	D	70,536	(706) 259-9441
Ocmulgee EMC	D	9,004	(912) 374-7001
Oconee EMC	D	9,595	(912) 676-3191
Oglethorpe Power Corporation	GT		(404) 270-7600
Okefenoke REMC	D	23,712	(912) 462-5131
Pataula EMC	D	4,083	(912) 732-3171
Planters EMC	D	12,788	(912) 982-4722
Rayle EMC	D	14,061	(706) 678-2116
Satilla REMC	D	36,569	(912) 632-7222
Sawnee EMC	D	59,837	(404) 887-2363
Slash Pine EMC	D	5,029	(912) 487-5201
Snapping Shoals EMC	D	43,193	(404) 786-3484
Southeastern Data Cooperative	O		(404) 414-8400
Sumter EMC	D	14,271	(912) 924-8041
Three Notch EMC	D	11,719	(912) 524-5377
Tri-County EMC	D	13,368	(912) 986-3134
Tri-State EMC	D	11,366	(706) 492-3251
Troup Electric Membership Corp.	D	19,475	(706) 845-2000

*See page 226 for Key

continued on page 194

GEORGIA *(continued)*

Name of Cooperative	Type*	Consumer Members	Phone Number
Upson County EMC	D	7,477	(706) 647-5475
Walton EMC	D	67,398	(404) 267-2505
Washington EMC	D	11,688	(912) 552-2577

IDAHO

Clearwater Power Company	D	7,799	(208) 743-1501
Fall River REC, Inc.	D	8,200	(208) 652-7431
Idaho Cooperative Utilities Assn.	S		(208) 645-2211
Idaho County Light & Power Co-op	D	2,374	(208) 983-1610
Kootenai Electric Co-op, Inc.	D	11,411	(208) 765-1200
Lost River Electric Co-op, Inc.	D	2,069	(208) 588-3311
Northern Lights, Inc.	D	11,531	(208) 263-5141
Raft River REC, Inc.	D	2,512	(208) 645-2211
Riverside Electric Company	D	483	(208) 436-3855
Rural Electric Company	D	2,433	(208) 436-4781
Salmon River Electric Co-op, Inc.	D	2,185	(208) 879-2283
South Side Electric Lines, Inc.	D	535	(208) 654-2313

ILLINOIS

Adams Electrical Co-operative	D	6,904	(217) 593-7701
Assn. Of Illinois Electric Co-ops	S		(217) 529-5561
Clay Electric Co-op, Inc.	D	2,946	(618) 662-2171
Clinton County Electric Co-op, Inc.	D	4,853	(618) 526-7282
Coles-Moultrie Electric Co-op	D	7,780	(217) 235-0341
Corn Belt Electric Co-op, Inc.	D	14,166	(309) 662-5330
Eastern Illinois Electric Co-op	D	12,710	(217) 379-2131
Edgar Electric Co-op Assn.	D	4,943	(217) 463-4154
Egyptian Electric Co-op Assn.	D	11,812	(618) 965-3434
Farmers Mutual Electric Company	D	1,265	(309) 944-4669

*See page 226 for Key

Name of Cooperative	Type*	Consumer Members	Phone Number
Illinois Rural Electric Co.	D	9,572	(217) 742-3128
Illinois Valley Electric Co-op	D	5,697	(815) 875-4488
Jo-Carroll Electric Co-op, Inc.	D	5,147	(815) 858-2207
M.J.M. Electric Co-op, Inc.	D	7,552	(217) 854-3137
McDonough Power Co-op	D	4,705	(309) 833-2101
Menard Electric Co-op	D	8,676	(217) 632-7746
Monroe County Electric Co-operative	D	4,809	(618) 939-7171
Norris Electric Co-op	D	16,494	(618) 783-8765
Rural Electric Convenience Co-op	D	4,921	(217) 438-6197
Shelby Electric Cooperative	D	8,724	(217) 774-3986
Southeastern Illinois Elec. Co-op	D	19,394	(618) 273-2611
Southern Illinois Electric Co-op	D	9,798	(618) 827-3555
Southern Illinois Power Co-op	GT		(618) 964-1448
Southwestern Electric Co-op, Inc.	D	14,904	(618) 664-1025
Soyland Power Cooperative	GT		(217) 423-0021
Spoon River Electric Co-op, Inc.	D	4,117	(309) 647-2700
Tri-County Electric Co-op, Inc.	D	13,274	(6180 244-5151
Wayne-White Counties Electric Co-op	D	13,131	(618) 842-2196
Western Illinois Electrical Co-op.	D	3,259	(217) 357-3125

INDIANA

Name of Cooperative	Type*	Consumer Members	Phone Number
Bartholomew County REMC	D	8,490	(812) 372-2546
Boone County REMC	D	6,612	(317) 482-2390
Carroll County REMC	D	5,722	(317) 564-2057
Central Indiana Power	D	7,270	(317) 462-4417
Clark County REMC	D	12,360	(812) 246-3316
Co-ops Federal Credit Union	O		(317) 248-0043
Daviess-Martin County REMC	D	6,891	(812) 254-1870
Decatur County REMC	D	5,900	(812) 663-3391
Dubois REC, Inc.	D	10,215	(812) 482-5454
Fulton County REMC	D	5,378	(219) 223-3156

*See page 226 for Key

continued on page 196

INDIANA *(continued)*

Name of Cooperative	Type*	Consumer Members	Phone Number
Harrison County REMC	D	15,444	(812) 738-4115
Hendricks County REMC	D	15,082	(317) 745-5473
Henry County REMC	O	7,692	(317) 529-1212
Hoosier Energy REC., Inc.	GT		(812) 876-2021
Indiana Statewide Assn. Of REC, Inc.	S		(317) 248-9453
Jackson County REMC	D	18,667	(812) 358-4458
Jasper County REMC	D	6,214	(219) 866-4601
Jay County REMC	D	5,030	(219) 726-7121
Johnson County REMC	D	11,652	(317) 736-6174
Kankakee Valley REMC	D	13,711	(219) 733-2511
Knox County REMC	D	8,769	(812) 882-5140
Kosciusko County REMC	D	13,932	(219) 267-6331
LaGrange County REMC	D	5,980	(219) 463-7165
Marshall County REMC	D	5,483	(219) 936-3161
Miami-Cass County REMC	D	3,953	(317) 473-6668
Newton County REMC	D	1,273	(219) 474-6224
Noble REMC	D	8,366	(219) 636-2113
Northeastern REMC	D	15,415	(219) 244-6111
Orange County REMC	D	5,908	(812) 865-2229
Parke County REMC	D	10,408	(317) 569-3133
Rush County REMC	D	4,755	(317) 932-4121
Shelby County REMC	D	6,822	(317) 398-6621
South Central Indiana REMC	D	24,780	(317) 342-3344
Southeastern Indiana REMC	D	19,087	(812) 689-4111
Southern Indiana REC, Inc.	D	7,399	(812) 547-2316
Steuben County REMC	D	7,216	(219) 665-3563
Sullivan County REMC	D	5,844	(812) 268-4366
Tipmont REMC	D	15,720	(317) 339-7211
United REMC	D	8,806	(219) 758-3155

*See page 226 for Key

Name of Cooperative	Type*	Consumer Members	Phone Number
Util. Dist. of Western Indiana REMC	D	15,252	(812) 384-4446
Wabash County REMC	D	4,643	(219) 563-2146
Wabash Valley Power Assn.	GT		(317) 481-2800
Warren County REMC	D	4,089	(317) 762-6114
White County REMC	D	7,108	(219) 583-7161
Whitewater Valley REMC	D	10,054	(317) 962-7521

IOWA

Name of Cooperative	Type*	Consumer Members	Phone Number
Adams County Co-op Electric Co.	D	1,694	(515) 322-3165
Allamakee-Clayton Elec. Co-op, Inc.	D	8,038	(319) 864-7611
Benton County Electric Co-op Assn.	D	3,450	(319) 472-2367
Boone Valley Electric Co-op	O	132	(515) 824-3565
Buchanan County RECC	D	3,491	(319) 334-2571
Butler County REC	D	4,785	(319) 267-2726
Calhoun County Electric Co-op Assn.	D	1,649	(712) 297-7112
Cedar Valley Electric Co-op	D	2,809	(515) 736-4965
Central Iowa Power Co-op	GT		(319) 366-8011
Chariton Valley Electric Co-op	D	5,388	(515) 932-7126
Clarke Electric Co-op, Inc.	D	4,196	(515) 342-2173
Corn Belt Power Co-op	GT		(515) 332-2571
Eastern Iowa Light & Power Co-op	D	19,584	(319) 732-2211
Farmers Electric Co-op-Kalona	D	601	(319) 683-2510
Farmers Electric Co-op, Inc.	D	4,674	(515) 743-6146
Franklin REC	D	1,786	(515) 456-2557
Glidden REC	D	1,659	(712) 659-3649
Grundy County REC	D	2,267	(319) 824-5251
Guthrie County RECA	D	4,483	(515) 747-2206
Hancock County REC	D	1,809	(515) 923-2654
Harrison County REC	D	3,000	(712) 647-2727
Hawkeye Tri-County REC	D	5,837	(319) 547-3801
Humboldt County REC	D	1,837	(515) 332-1616

*See page 226 for Key

continued on page 198

IOWA *(continued)*

Name of Cooperative	Type*	Consumer Members	Phone Number
Ida County REC	D	1,160	(712) 364-3341
Iowa Area Development Group	O		(515) 223-4817
Iowa Assn. of Electric Co-ops	S		(515) 276-5350
Iowa Lakes Electric Cooperative	D	11,064	(712) 362-2694
L & O Power Co-op	GT		(712) 472-2532
Linn County REC	D	11,383	(319) 377-1587
Lyon REC	D	1,798	(712) 472-2506
Maquoketa Valley REC	D	11,539	(319) 462-3542
Marshall County REC	D	3,955	(515) 752-1593
Midland Power Cooperative	D	8,086	(515) 386-4111
Monona County REC	D	2,311	(712) 423-1622
Nishnabotna Valley REC	D	3,534	(712) 755-2166
North Iowa Municipal Electric	O		(515) 332-2981
North West Rural Electric Co-op	D	3,524	(712) 737-4935
Northwest Iowa Power Co-op	GT		(712) 546-4141
Nyman Electric Co-op, Inc.	D	1,429	(712) 829-2211
Osceola Electric Co-op, Inc.	D	1,154	(712) 754-2519
Pella Co-op Electric Assn.	D	2,007	(515) 628-1040
Plymouth Electric Co-op Assn.	D	3,030	(712) 546-4149
Rideta Electric Co-op, Inc.	D	2,596	(515) 464-2244
S.E. Iowa Co-op Electric Assn.	D	7,397	(319) 385-1577
Sac County REC	D	1,072	(712) 662-4275
Winnebago RECA	D	2,010	(515) 584-2251
Woodbury County RECA	D	2,633	(712) 873-3125
Wright County REC	D	2,309	(515) 532-2805

KANSAS

Name of Cooperative	Type*	Consumer Members	Phone Number
Ark Valley Electric Co-op Assn.	D	4,479	(316) 662-6661
Brown-Atchison Electric Co-op Assn.	D	2,853	(913) 486-2117

*See page 226 for Key

Name of Cooperative	Type*	Consumer Members	Phone Number
Butler RECA, Inc.	D	5,503	(316) 321-9600
C. & W. Rural Electric Co-op Assn.	D	2,778	(913) 632-3111
C.M.S. Electric Co-op, Inc.	D	4,371	(316) 873-2184
Caney Valley Electric Co-op Assn.	D	5,315	(316) 758-2262
Doniphan Electric Co-op Assn., Inc.	D	1,469	(913) 985-3523
DS&O Rural Electric Co-op Assn.	D	6,401	(913) 655-2011
Federated RE Insurance Corp.	O		(913) 541-0150
Flint Hills RECA, Inc.	D	5,770	(316) 767-5144
Jewell-Mitchell Co-op Electric Co.	D	4,640	(913) 378-3151
Kansas Electric Co-ops, Inc.	S		(913) 478-4554
Kansas Electric Power Co-op	GT		(913) 273-7010
Kansas Municipal Energy Agency	O		(913) 677-2885
Kaw Valley Elec. Co-op, Inc.	D	6,355	(913) 272-4330
Lane-Scott Electric Co-op, Inc.	D	2,453	(316) 397-2321
Leavenworth-Jefferson Elec. Co-op	D	6,200	(913) 796-6111
Lyon-Coffey Electric Co-op	D	6,322	(316) 364-2116
Midwest Energy, Inc.	D	34,420	(913) 625-3437
N.C.K. Electric Co-op, Inc.	D	2,979	(913) 527-2251
Nemaha-Marshall Electric Co-op	D	3,147	(913) 736-2345
Ninnescah RECA, Inc.	D	3,141	(316) 672-5538
Northwest Kansas Elec. Co-op Assn.	D	1,982	(913) 734-2311
Norton-Decatur Co-op Electric Co.	D	5,900	(913) 877-3323
Pioneer Electric Co-op	D	11,265	(316) 356-1211
PR&W Electric Co-op Assn.	D	2,987	(913) 456-2212
Radiant Electric Co-op, Inc.	D	3,426	(316) 378-2161
Rural Data Processing Association	O		(913) 235-0594
Sedgwick County Electric Co-op	D	4,013	(316) 542-3131
Sunflower Electric Power Corp.	GT		(913) 628-2845
Twin Valley Electric Co-op	D	2,199	(316) 784-5500
United Electric Cooperative, Inc.	D	5,454	(316) 365-5151
Victory Electric Co-op Assn., Inc.	D	3,620	(316) 227-2139

*See page 226 for Key

continued on page 200

KANSAS *(continued)*

Name of Cooperative	Type*	Consumer Members	Phone Number
Western Co-op Electric Assn., Inc.	D	4,338	(913) 743-5561
Wheatland Electric Co-op, Inc.	D	14,429	(316) 872-5885

KENTUCKY

Name of Cooperative	Type*	Consumer Members	Phone Number
Big Rivers Electric Corp.	GT		(502) 827-2561
Big Sandy RECC	D	10,684	(606) 789-4095
Blue Grass RECC	D	17,306	(606) 885-4191
Clark RECC	D	18,473	(606) 744-4251
Cumberland Valley RECC	D	17,985	(606) 528-2677
East Kentucky Power Co-op	GT		(606) 744-4812
Farmers RECC	D	17,296	(502) 651-2193
Fleming-Mason RECC	D	17,346	(606) 845-2661
Fox Creek RECC	D	8,837	(502) 839-3442
Grayson RECC	D	12,141	(606) 474-5136
Green River Electric Corp.	D	26,942	(502) 926-4141
Harrison County RECC	D	10,620	(606) 234-3131
Henderson Union Electric Co-op	D	16,984	(502) 826-3991
Hickman-Fulton Counties RECC	D	3,577	(502) 236-2521
Inter-County RECC	D	17,787	(606) 236-4561
Jackson County RECC	D	39,391	(606) 287-7161
Jackson Purchase Elec. Co-op Corp.	D	22,253	(502) 442-7321
Kentucky Assn. of Elec. Co-ops	S		(502) 451-2430
Licking Valley RECC	D	13,722	(606) 743-3179
Meade County RECC	D	19.855	(502) 422-2162
Nolin RECC	D	21,971	(502) 765-6153
Owen Electric Cooperative, Inc.	D	32,391	(502) 484-3471
Pennyrile RECC	D	36,398	(502) 886-2555
Salt River Electric Co-op Corp.	D	26,806	(502) 348-3931
Shelby RECC	D	9,779	(502) 633-4420

*See page 226 for Key

Name of Cooperative	Type*	Consumer Members	Phone Number
South Kentucky RECC	D	46,279	(606) 678-4121
Taylor County RECC	D	18,767	(502) 465-4101
United Utility Supply Co-op	O		(502) 459-4011
Warren RECC	D	43,476	(502) 842-6541
West Kentucky RECC	D	31,410	(502) 247-1321

LOUISIANA

Assn. of Louisiana Electric Co-ops	S		(504) 293-3450
Beauregard Electric Co-op, Inc.	D	29,807	(318) 463-6221
Cajun Electric Power Co-op	GT		(504) 291-3060
Claiborne Electric Co-op, Inc.	D	19,602	(318) 927-3504
Concordia Electric Co-op, Inc.	D	11,231	(318) 339-7969
DEMCO	D	60,787	(504) 261-1221
Dixie Business Dev. Center, Inc.	O		(504) 665-0809
Enterprise Center of Louisiana	O		(318) 896-9115
Jefferson Davis Electric Co-op	D	8,660	(318) 824-4330
Northeast Louisiana Power Co-op	D	13,686	(318) 435-4523
Pointe Coupee EMC	D	8,670	(504) 638-3751
South Louisiana Electric Co-op	D	15,111	(504) 876-6880
Southwest Louisiana EMC	D	65,952	(318) 896-5384
Teche Electric Co-op, Inc.	D	8,703	(318) 276-6347
Valley EMC	D	34,356	(318) 352-3601
Washington-St. Tammany Elec. Co-op	D	30,197	(504) 839-3562

MAINE

Eastern Maine Electric Co-op, Inc.	D	11,179	(207) 454-7555
Fox Islands Electric Co-op	D	1,538	(207) 863-4636
Swans Island Electric Co-op	O	502	(207) 526-4336
Union River Electric Co-op, Inc.	D	1,818	(207) 584-3200

*See page 226 for Key

MARYLAND

Name of Cooperative	Type*	Consumer Members	Phone Number
Choptank Electric Co-op, Inc.	D	30,952	(410) 479-0380
Great Lakes Elec. Consumers Assn.	O		(301) 963-5533
Southern Maryland Electric Co-op	D	99,062	(301) 274-3111

MASSACHUSETTS

Northeast Public Power Assn.	O		(508) 898-3554

MICHIGAN

Alger-Delta Co-op Electric Assn.	D	8,199	(906) 428-4141
Cherryland Electric Cooperative	D	22,396	(616) 943-8377
Cloverland Electric Co-op	D	14,670	(906) 635-6800
Fruit Belt Electric Co-op	D	23,186	(616) 445-2477
Michigan Electric Co-op Assn.	S		(517) 351-6322
O & A Electric Co-op, Inc.	D	25,895	(616) 652-1651
Oceana Electric Co-op	D	9,618	(616) 873-2155
Ontonagon County REA	D	3,806	(906) 884-4151
Presque Isle Electric & Gas Co-op	D	26,454	(517) 733-8515
Southeastern Michigan REC, Inc.	D	4,262	(517) 263-1808
Thumb Electric Co-op, Inc.	D	10,363	(517) 658-8571
Top O'Michigan Rural Elec. Co.	D	42,593	(616) 582-6521
Tri-County Electric Co-op	D	19,436	(517) 647-7554
Western Michigan Electric Co-op	D	11,103	(616) 757-4724
Wolverine Power Supply Co-op	GT		(616) 775-5700

MINNESOTA

Agralite Cooperative	D	4,701	(612) 843-4150
Anoka Electric Co-op	D	76,233	(612) 323-2600
Arrowhead Electric Co-op, Inc.	D	2,843	(218) 663-7239
Beltrami Electric Co-op, Inc.	D	13,650	(218) 751-2540

*See page 226 for Key

Name of Cooperative	Type*	Consumer Members	Phone Number
Brown County REA	D	3,382	(507) 794-3331
Carlton County Co-op Power Assn.	D	10,205	(218) 273-4111
Clearwater-Polk Electric Co-op	D	3,394	(218) 694-6241
Co-op Light & Power Association	D	4,229	(218) 834-2226
Cooperative Power	GT		(612) 937-8599
Cooperative Response Center, Inc.	O		(507) 437-8867
Crow Wing Co-op Power & Light Co.	D	28,601	(218) 829-2827
Dairyland Electric Co-op, Inc.	D	12,921	(218) 326-6671
Dakota Electric Association	D	67,332	(612) 463-7134
East Central Electric Assn.	D	27,325	(612) 396-3351
Federated REA	D	4,694	(507) 847-3520
Freeborn-Mower Electric Co-op	D	5,470	(507) 373-6421
Frost-BENCO-Wells Elec. Assn.	D	10,113	(507) 387-7963
Goodhue County Co-op	D	3,825	(507) 732-5117
Itasca-Mantrap Co-op Elec. Assn.	D	7,930	(218) 732-3377
Kandiyohi Co-op Elec. Power Assn.	D	6,649	(612) 235-4155
Lake Region Co-op Electrical Assn	D	20,149	(218) 863-1171
Lyon-Lincoln Electric Co-op, Inc.	D	3,712	(507) 247-5505
McLeod Co-op Power Assn.	D	5,470	(612) 864-3148
Meeker Co-op Light & Power Assn.	D	6,676	(612) 693-3231
Mille Lacs Electric Co-op	D	11,474	(218) 927-2191
Minn. Valley Co-op L. & P. Assn.	D	5,153	(612) 269-2163
Minnesota Rural Electric Assn.	S		(612) 424-1020
Minnesota Valley Electric Co-op	D	16,696	(612) 492-2313
Nobles Cooperative Electric	D	4,786	(507) 372-7331
North Itasca Electric Co-op	D	4,119	(218) 743-3131
North Pine Electric Co-op, Inc.	D	8,230	(612) 233-6311
North Star Electric Co-op, Inc.	D	5,323	(218) 634-2202
Northern Electric Co-op Assn.	D	15,784	(218) 741-8137
P.K.M. Electric Co-op, Inc.	D	3,705	(218) 745-4711
People's Co-op Power Assn.	D	13,722	(507) 288-4004

*See page 226 for Key

continued on page 204

MINNESOTA *(continued)*

Name of Cooperative	Type*	Consumer Members	Phone Number
Red Lake Electric Co-op, Inc.	D	4,696	(218) 253-2168
Red River Valley Co-op Power Assn.	D	4,220	(218) 456-2139
Redwood Electric Co-op	D	2,394	(507) 692-2214
Renville-Sibley Co-op Power Assn.	D	1,948	(612) 826-2593
Roseau Electric Co-op, Inc.	D	5,171	(218) 463-1543
Runestone Electric Assn.	D	10,101	(612) 762-1121
South Central Electric Assn.	D	3,757	(507) 375-3164
Southwestern Minnesota Co-op Elec.	D	2,688	(507) 825-3341
Stearns Co-op Electric Assn.	D	16,090	(612) 256-4241
Steele-Waseca Co-op Electric	D	6,930	(507) 451-7340
Todd-Wadena Electric Co-op	D	6,294	(218) 631-3120
Traverse Electric Co-op, Inc.	D	2,556	(612) 563-8616
Tri-County Electric Co-op	D	11,030	(507) 864-7783
United Power Association	GT		(612) 441-3121
Wild Rice Electric Co-op, Inc.	D	10,963	(218) 935-2517
Wright-Hennepin Co-op Elec. Assn.	D	26,817	(612) 963-3131

MISSISSIPPI

Name of Cooperative	Type*	Consumer Members	Phone Number
Alcorn County Electric Power Assn.	O		(601) 287-4402
Central Electric Power Assn.	D	24,117	(601) 267-5671
Central Service Association	O		(601) 842-5962
Coahoma Electric Power Assn.	D	6,032	(601) 624-8321
Coast Electric Power Assn.	D	46,189	(601) 467-6535
Delta Electric Power Assn.	D	21,105	(601) 453-6352
Dixie Electric Power Assn.	D	27,332	(601) 425-2535
East Mississippi EPA	D	28,675	(601) 483-7361
Electric Power Assn. of Mississippi	S		(601) 922-2341
Four County Electric Power Assn.	D	36,675	(601) 327-8900
Magnolia Electric Power Assn.	D	21,775	(601) 684-4011

*See page 226 for Key

Name of Cooperative	Type*	Consumer Members	Phone Number
Montoe County Electric Power Assn.	O	9,129	(601) 256-2962
Natchez Trace Electric Power	D	14,425	(601) 456-3037
North Central Mississippi EPA	D	11,953	(601) 838-2151
North East Mississippi EPA	D	11,765	(601) 234-6331
Pearl River Valley Elec. Power Assn.	D	28,087	(601) 736-2666
Pontotoc Electric Power Assn.	D	14,683	(601) 489-3211
Prentiss County Elec. Power Assn.	D	11,995	(601) 728-4433
Singing River Elec. Power Assn.	D	46,825	(601) 947-4211
South Mississippi Elec. Power	GT		(601) 268-2083
Southern Pine Elec. Power Assn.	D	48,830	(601) 785-6511
Southwest Mississippi EPA	D	20,935	(601) 437-3611
Tallahatchie Valley EPA	D	21,472	(601) 563-4742
Tippah Electric Power Assn.	O	10,466	(601) 837-8139
Tishomingo County EPA	D	11,814	(601) 423-3646
Tombigbee Electric Power Assn.	O	31,086	(601) 842-7635
Twin County Electric Power Assn.	D	11,669	(601) 827-2262
Yazoo Valley Electric Power Assn.	D	8,783	(601) 746-4251

MISSOURI

Name of Cooperative	Type*	Consumer Members	Phone Number
Assn. of Missouri Electric Co-ops	S		(314) 635-6857
Associated Electric Co-op, Inc.	GT		(417) 881-1204
Atchison-Holt Electric Co-op	D	3,557	(816) 744-5344
Barry Electric Co-op	D	7,548	(417) 847-2131
Barton County Electric Co-op	D	5,129	(417) 682-5634
Black River Electric Co-op	D	20,803	(314) 783-3381
Boone Electric Co-op	D	20,858	(314) 449-4181
Callaway Electric Co-op	D	9,042	(314) 642-3326
Central Area Data Processing Co-op	O		(314) 922-9158
Central Electric Power Co-op	GT		(314) 634-2454
Central Missouri Electric Co-op	D	7,724	(816) 826-2900
Citizens Electric Corp.	D	20,284	(314) 883-3511

*See page 226 for Key

continued on page 206

MISSOURI *(continued)*

Name of Cooperative	Type*	Consumer Members	Phone Number
Co-Mo Electric Co-op, Inc.	D	22,962	(816) 433-5521
Consolidated Electric Co-op	D	6,521	(314) 581-3630
Crawford Electric Co-op, Inc.	D	14,830	(314) 732-4415
Cuivre River Electric Co-op, Inc.	D	32,982	(314) 528-8261
Farmers Electric Co-op, Inc.	D	10,349	(816) 646-4281
Gascosage Electric Co-op	D	7,254	(314) 759-7146
Grundy Electric Co-op, Inc.	D	7,525	(816) 359-3941
Howard Electric Co-op	D	2,452	(816) 248-3311
Howell-Oregon Electric Co-op, Inc.	D	18,416	(417) 256-2131
Intercounty Electric Co-op Assn.	D	24,596	(314) 674-2211
Laclede Electric Co-op	D	23,925	(417) 532-3164
Lewis County RECA	D	5,682	(314) 497-2281
M & A Electric Power Co-op	GT		(314) 785-9651
Macon Electric Co-op	D	8,055	(816) 385-3157
Missouri Joint Municipal Electric	D		(314) 445-3279
Missouri REC	D	4,051	(314) 769-2104
N.W. Electric Power Co-op, Inc.	GT		(816) 632-2121
National Food & Energy Council	O		(314) 875-7155
New-Mac Electric Co-op, Inc.	D	12,079	(417) 451-1515
Nodaway-Worth Electric Co-op, Inc.	D	3,525	(816) 582-2837
North Central Missouri Elec. Co-op	D	3,967	(816) 265-4404
Northeast Missouri Elec. Power	GT		(314) 769-2107
Northwest Missouri Electric Co-op	D	5,265	(816) 324-3155
Osage Valley Electric Co-op Assn.	D	12,182	(816) 679-3131
Ozark Border Electric Co-op	D	28,632	(314) 785-4631
Ozark Electric Co-op	D	20,759	(417) 466-2144
Pemiscot-Dunklin Electric Co-op	D	5,470	(314) 757-6641
Platte-Clay Electric Co-op, Inc.	D	12,567	(816) 431-2131
Ralls County Electric Co-op	D	4,397	(314) 985-8711

*See page 226 for Key

Name of Cooperative	Type*	Consumer Members	Phone Number
Rural Missouri Cable T.V., Inc.	O		(417) 334-7897
Sac-Osage Electric Co-op, Inc.	D	8,450	(417) 876-2721
Scott-New Madrid-Miss. Elec. Co-op	D	12,826	(314) 471-5821
Se-Ma-No Electric Co-op	D	4,319	(417) 924-3243
Sho-Me Power Electric Cooperative	GT		(417) 468-2615
Southwest Electric Co-op	D	27,530	(417) 326-5244
Three Rivers Electric Co-op	D	15,845	(314) 897-2251
Tri-County Electric Co-op Assn.	D	5,352	(816) 457-3733
Webster Electric Co-op	D	12,064	(417) 859-2216
West Central Electric Co-op, Inc.	D	10,254	(816) 584-2131
White River Valley Elec. Co-op	D	27,155	(417) 335-9335

MONTANA

Name of Cooperative	Type*	Consumer Members	Phone Number
Beartooth Electric Co-op, Inc.	D	3,768	(406) 446-2310
Big Flat Electric Co-op, Inc.	D	1,542	(406) 654-2040
Big Horn County Electric Co-op	D	3,238	(406) 665-2830
Central Montana Elec. Power Co-op	GT		(406) 248-7936
Fergus Electric Co-op, Inc.	D	4,997	(406) 538-3465
Flathead Electric Co-op, Inc.	D	10,226	(406) 752-4483
Glacier Electric Co-op, Inc.	D	6,550	(406) 873-5566
Goldenwest Electric Co-op, Inc.	D	1,113	(406) 795-2423
Hill County Electric Co-op, Inc.	D	3,103	(406) 265-7804
InterBel Telephone Co-op	O		(406) 889-3301
Lincoln Electric Co-op, Inc.	D	3,053	(406) 889-3301
Lower Yellowstone REA, Inc.	D	3,732	(406) 482-1602
Marias River Electric Co-op, Inc.	D	3,686	(406) 434-5575
McCone Electric Co-op, Inc.	D	4,651	(406) 485-3430
Mid-Yellowstone Electric Co-op	D	1,741	(406) 342-5521
Missoula Electric Co-op, Inc.	D	9,015	(406) 721-4433
Montana Electric Co-ops' Assn.	S		(406) 761-8333
Montana Telephone Association	O		(406) 761-8335

*See page 226 for Key

continued on page 208

MONTANA *(continued)*

Name of Cooperative	Type*	Consumer Members	Phone Number
Northern Electric Co-op, Inc.	D	1,232	(406) 762-3411
Park Electric Co-op, Inc.	D	3,455	(406) 222-3100
Ravalli County Electric Co-op, Inc.	D	5,577	(406) 961-3001
Sheridan Electric Co-op, Inc.	D	3,096	(406) 789-2231
Southeast Electric Co-op, Inc.	D	1,780	(406) 775-8762
Sun River Electric Co-op, Inc.	D	4,509	(406) 467-2526
Tongue River Electric Co-op, Inc.	D	4,358	(406) 784-2341
Upper Missouri G&T Electric Co-op	GT		(406) 482-4100
Valley Electric Co-op, Inc.	D	1,691	(406) 367-5315
Vigilante Electric Co-op, Inc.	D	5,917	(406) 683-2327
Western Montana Electric G&T Co-op	GT		(406) 721-0945
Yellowstone Valley Electric Co-op	D	10,455	(406) 348-3411

NEBRASKA

Name of Cooperative	Type*	Consumer Members	Phone Number
Burt County PPD	D	3,755	(402) 374-2631
Butler County RPPD	D	4,123	(402) 367-3081
Cedar-Knox PPD	D	4,464	(402) 254-6291
Central Nebraska PPID	O		(308) 995-8601
Chimney Rock PPD	D	2,223	(308) 586-1824
Cornhusker PPD	D	7,677	(402) 564-2821
Cuming County PPD	D	2,739	(402) 372-2463
Custer PPD	D	8,507	(308) 872-2451
Dawson County PPD	D	16,018	(308) 324-2386
Elkhorn RPPD	D	6,714	(402) 675-2185
Howard Greeley RPPD	D	3,109	(308) 754-4457
KBR Rural Public Power District	D	3,202	(402) 387-1120
Northeast Nebraska RPPD	D	2,733	(402) 695-2642
Northwest RPPD	D	2,721	(308) 638-4445
Panhandle REMA	D	3,331	(308) 762-1311

*See page 226 for Key

Name of Cooperative	Type*	Consumer Members	Phone Number
Polk County RPPD	D	2,544	(402) 764-4381
Roosevelt PPD	D	2,384	(308) 623-2124
Seward County RPPD	D	2,618	(402) 643-2951
South Central PPD	D	4,330	(402) 225-2351
Southern Nebraska RPPD	D	18,662	(308) 384-2350
Southwest PPD	D	5,228	(308) 285-3295
Stanton County PPD	D	2,909	(402) 439-2228
Twin Valleys PPD	D	4,597	(308) 697-3315
Wayne County PPD	D	2,689	(402) 375-1360
Wheat Belt PPD	D	4,397	(308) 254-5871
York County RPPD	D	4,541	(402) 362-3355

NEVADA

Name of Cooperative	Type*	Consumer Members	Phone Number
Alamo Power District #3	O	481	(702) 725-3335
Lincoln County Power District #1	O	180	(702) 962-5122
Mt. Wheeler Power, Inc.	D	5,848	(702) 289-8981
Nevada Co-op Credit Union	O		(702) 752-3956
Overton Power District No. 5	D	3,787	(702) 397-2512
Valley Electric Association	D	8,083	(702) 727-5312
Wells REC	D	4,398	(702) 752-3328

NEW HAMPSHIRE

Name of Cooperative	Type*	Consumer Members	Phone Number
New Hampshire Electric Cooperative	D	65,396	(603) 536-1800
Northeastern Assn. of Elec. Co-ops	O		(603) 536-1800

NEW JERSEY

Name of Cooperative	Type*	Consumer Members	Phone Number
Sussex REC	D	10,059	(201) 875-5101

*See page 226 for Key

NEW MEXICO *(continued)*

Name of Cooperative	Type*	Consumer Members	Phone Number
Central New Mexico Elec. Co-op	D	10,663	(505) 847-2521
Central Valley Electric Co-op, Inc.	D	8,728	(505) 746-3571
Columbus Electric Co-op, Inc.	D	3,300	(505) 546-8838
Continental Divide Electric Co-op	D	19,121	(505) 285-6656
Cooperative Services, Inc.	O		(505) 474-4755
Farmers Electric Co-op, Inc.	D	9,506	(505) 769-2116
Jemez Mountains Electric Co-op	D	23,691	(505) 753-2105
Kit Carson Electric Co-op, Inc.	D	19,211	(505) 758-2258
Lea County Electric Co-op, Inc.	D	12,524	(505) 396-3631
Mora-San Miguel Electric Co-op	D	7,375	(505) 387-2205
New Mexico RECA	S		(505) 982-4671
Northern Rio Arriba Elec. Co-op	D	3,125	(505) 756-2181
Otero County Electric Co-op, Inc.	D	11,608	(505) 682-2521
Plains Electric G&T Co-op	GT		(505) 884-1881
Roosevelt County Electric Co-op	D	5,189	(505) 356-4491
Sierra Electric Co-op	D	2,877	(505) 744-5231
Socorro Electric Co-op, Inc.	D	8,666	(505) 835-0560
Southwestern Electric Co-op, Inc.	D	1,441	(505) 374-2451
Springer Electric Co-op, Inc.	D	2,413	(505) 483-2421

NEW YORK

Name of Cooperative	Type*	Consumer Members	Phone Number
Delaware County Electric Co-op	D	4,266	(607) 746-2341
New York State RECA	S		(607) 293-6622
Oneida-Madison Electric Co-op, Inc.	D	1,511	(315) 893-1851
Ostego Electric Co-op, Inc.	D	3,447	(607) 293-6622
Steuben REC, Inc.	D	5,081	(607) 776-4161

*See page 226 for Key

NORTH CAROLINA

Name of Cooperative	Type*	Consumer Members	Phone Number
Albemarle EMC	D	8,301	(919) 426-5735
Blue Ridge EMC	D	51,870	(704) 758-2383
Brunswick EMC	D	47,617	(910) 754-4391
Cape Hatteras Electric Co-op	D	4,921	(919) 995-5616
Carolina Electric Cooperatives	GT		(919) 872-0800
Carteret-Craven Electric Co-op	D	26,345	(919) 247-3107
Central EMC	D	10,554	(919) 774-4900
Crescent EMC	D	41,023	(704) 873-5241
Davidson EMC	D	31,642	(704) 249-3131
Edgecombe-Martin County EMC	D	9,992	(919) 823-2171
EMC Employees Credit Union	O		(919) 872-2395
Four County EMC	D	23,595	(910) 259-2171
French Broad EMC	D	26,076	(704) 649-2051
Halifax EMC	D	9,572	(919) 445-5111
Harkers Island EMC	D	1,185	(919) 728-2593
Haywood EMC	D	16,675	(704) 452-2281
Jones-Onslow EMC	D	39,599	(910) 353-1940
Lumbee River EMC	D	32,585	(910) 843-4131
N.C. Assn. of Electric Co-ops	O		(919) 872-0800
Pee Dee EMC	D	16,664	(704) 694-2114
Piedmont EMC	D	21,089	(919) 732-2123
Pitt & Greene EMC	D	7,023	(919) 753-3128
Randolph EMC	D	23,256	(910) 625-5177
Roanoke Electric Co-op	D	12,593	(919) 539-2236
Rutherford EMC	D	47,282	(704) 245-1621
South River EMC	D	28,827	(910) 892-8071
Surry-Yadkin EMC	D	19,883	(910) 386-8241
Tideland EMC	D	18,602	(919) 943-3046
Tri-County EMC	D	16,337	(919) 735-2611

*See page 226 for Key

continued on page 212

NORTH CAROLINA *(continued)*

Name of Cooperative	Type*	Consumer Members	Phone Number
Union EMC	D	30,400	(704) 289-3145
Wake EMC	D	15,154	(919) 554-6300

NORTH DAKOTA

Name of Cooperative	Type*	Consumer Members	Phone Number
Baker Electric Co-op, Inc.	D	5,637	(701) 968-3314
Basin Electric Power Co-op, Inc.	GT		(701) 223-0441
Burke-Divide Electric Co-op, Inc.	D	2,235	(701) 939-6671
Capital Electric Co-op, Inc.	D	7,222	(701) 223-1513
Cass County Electric Co-op, Inc.	D	14,761	(701) 428-3292
Cavalier REC, Inc.	D	1,556	(701) 256-5511
Central Power Electric Co-op, Inc.	GT		(701) 852-4407
James Valley Electric Co-op, Inc.	D	3,232	(701) 493-2281
KEM Electric Co-op, Inc.	D	3,306	(701) 254-4666
McKenzie Electric Co-op, Inc.	D	4,985	(701) 842-2311
McLean Electric Co-op, Inc.	D	2,738	(701) 463-2291
Minnkota Power Co-op, Inc.	GT		(701) 795-4000
Mor-Gran-Sou Electric Co-op, Inc.	D	5,313	(701) 597-3301
Mountrail-Williams Electric Co-op	D	6,159	(701) 572-3765
Nokak Electric Co-op, Inc.	D	11,384	(701) 746-4461
North Central Data Cooperative	O		(701) 663-6511
North Central Electric Co-op, Inc.	D	6,512	(701) 228-2202
North Dakota Association of REC's	S		(701) 663-6501
Oliver-Mercer Electric Co-op, Inc.	D	3,555	(701) 748-2293
R.S.R. Electric Co-op, Inc.	D	2,496	(701) 427-5242
Sheyenne Valley Electric Co-op	D	2,739	(701) 524-1110
Slope Electric Co-op, Inc.	D	2,996	(701) 579-4191
Square Butte Electric Cooperative	GT		(701) 795-4000
Tri-County Electric Co-op, Inc.	D	4,926	(701) 652-3156

*See page 226 for Key

Name of Cooperative	Type*	Consumer Members	Phone Number
Verendrye Electric Co-op, Inc.	D	8,468	(701) 338-2855
West Plains Electric Co-op, Inc.	D	5,528	(701) 225-5111

OHIO

Adams REC, Inc.	D	5,935	(513) 544-2305
Buckeye Power, Inc.	GT		(614) 846-5757
Buckeye REC, Inc.	D	15,753	(614) 446-1532
Butler REC, Inc.	D	8,164	(513) 867-4400
Carroll Electric Co-op, Inc.	D	9,690	(216) 627-2116
Darke REC, Inc.	D	4,426	(513) 548-4114
Delaware REC, Inc.	D	4,079	(614) 363-2641
Firelands Electric Co-op, Inc.		7,265	(419) 929-1571
Frontier Power Company	D	6,808	(614) 622-6755
Guernsey-Muskingum Electric Co-op	D	12,440	(614) 826-7661
Hancock-Wood Electric Co-op, Inc.	D	9,127	(419) 257-3241
Highland County Water Company, Inc.	O		(513) 393-4281
Holmes-Wayne Electric Co-op, Inc.	D	12,594	(216) 674-1055
Licking Rural Electrification, Inc.	D	17,057	(614) 892-2791
Logan Co. Co-op Pwr. & Light Assn.	D	3,645	(513) 592-4781
Lorain-Medina REC, Inc.	D	11,461	(216) 647-2133
Marion REC, Inc.	D	3,325	(614) 382-1234
Midwest Electric, Inc.	D	8,581	(419) 394-4110
Morrow Electric Co-op, Inc.	D	6,823	(419) 947-3055
North Central Electric Co-op, Inc.	D	8,298	(419) 426-3072
North Western Electric Co-op, Inc.	D	4,776	(419) 636-5051
Ohio REC, Inc.	S		(614) 846-5757
Paulding-Putnam Electric Co-op	D	10,165	(419) 399-5015
Pioneer REC, Inc.	D	13,154	(513) 773-2523
South Central Power Company	D	78,033	(614) 653-4422
Tricounty REC, Inc.	D	3,731	(419) 256-7900
Union REC, Inc.		4,792	(513) 642-1947

*See page 226 for Key

continued on page 214

OHIO *(continued)*

Name of Cooperative	Type*	Consumer Members	Phone Number
United Rural Electric, Inc.	D	3,615	(419) 673-7289
Washington Electric Co-op, Inc.	D	8,862	(614) 373-2141

OKLAHOMA

Name of Cooperative	Type*	Consumer Members	Phone Number
Alfalfa Electric Cooperative, Inc.	D	7,864	(405) 596-3575
Caddo Electric Co-op	D	14,887	(405) 656-2322
Canadian Valley Electric Co-op	D	17,831	(405) 382-3680
Central REC	D	13,351	(405) 372-2884
Choctaw Electric Co-op, Inc.	D	14,185	(405) 326-6486
Cimarron Electric Co-op	D	10,721	(405) 375-4121
Cookson Hills Electric Co-op, Inc.	D	13,133	(918) 967-4614
Cotton Electric Co-op	D	17,726	(405) 875-3351
East Central Oklahoma Elec. Co-op	D	24,310	(918) 756-0833
Great Plains Economic Development	O		(405) 667-5553
Harmon Electric Assn., Inc.	D	3,050	(405) 688-3342
Indian Electric Co-op, Inc.	D	16,641	(918) 358-2514
KAMO Power	GT		(918) 256-5551
Kay Electric Cooperative	D	5,861	(405) 363-1260
Kiamichi Electric Co-op, Inc.	D	15,546	(918) 465-2338
Kiwash Electric Co-op, Inc.	D	5,768	(405) 832-3361
Lake Region Electric Co-op, Inc.	D	18,084	(918) 772-2526
Northeast Oklahoma Electric Co-op	D	28,179	(918) 256-6405
Northfork Electric Cooperative	D	5,151	(405) 928-3366
Northwestern Electric Co-op, Inc.	D	9,084	(405) 256-7425
Oklahoma Assn. of Electric Co-op's	S		(405) 478-1455
Oklahoma Electric Co-op	D	28,067	(405) 321-2024
People's Electric Cooperative	D	16,288	(405) 332-3031
Red River Valley REA	D	10,606	(405) 276-3364
Rural Electric Cooperative, Inc.	D	8,607	(405) 756-3104

*See page 226 for Key

Name of Cooperative	Type*	Consumer Members	Phone Number
Southeastern Electric Co-op, Inc.	D	9,738	(405) 924-2170
Southwest Rural Electric Assn.	D	6,952	(405) 667-5281
Southwestern Power Resources Assn.	O		(405) 340-1900
Tri-County Electric Co-op, Inc.	D	9,905	(405) 652-2418
Verdigris Valley Electric Co-op	D	21,859	(918) 371-2584
Western Farmers Electric Co-op	GT		(405) 247-3351

OREGON

Name of Cooperative	Type*	Consumer Members	Phone Number
Blachly-Lane Co. Co-op Elec. Assn.	D	3,068	(503) 688-8711
Central Electric Co-op, Inc.	D	18,368	(503) 548-2144
Columbia Basin Electric Co-op	D	3,375	(503) 676-9146
Columbia Power Co-op Association	D	1,566	(503) 934-2311
Columbia River Alliance	O		(503) 238-1540
Consumers Power, Inc.	D	17,147	(503) 929-3124
Coos-Curry Electric Co-op, Inc.	D	14,502	(503) 332-3931
Douglas Electric Co-op, Inc.	D	8,182	(503) 673-6616
Emerald People's Utility District	O		(503) 746-1583
Harney Electric Co-op, Inc.	D	2,966	(503) 573-2061
Hood River Electric Cooperative	O	2,840	(503) 354-1233
Lane Electric Co-op	D	10,885	(503) 484-1151
Midstate Electric Co-op, Inc.	D	12,316	(503) 536-2126
Northern Wasco County P.U.D.	D	8,638	(503) 296-2226
Northwest Irrigation Utilities	O		(503) 233-5823
Oregon Development Group	O		(503) 362-7726
Oregon RECA	S		(503) 585-9988
Oregon Trail Elec. Consumers Co-op	D	25,999	(503) 523-6671
Pacific Northwest Generating Co-op	GT		(503) 288-1234
Public Power Council	O		(503) 232-2427
Ruralite Services, Inc.	O		(503) 357-2105
Salem Electric	O	12,600	(503) 362-3601
Tillamook P.U.D.	D	16,032	(503) 842-2535

*See page 226 for Key

continued on page 216

OREGON *(continued)*

Name of Cooperative	Type*	Consumer Members	Phone Number
Umatilla Electric Co-op Assn.	D	9,685	(503) 567-6414
Wasco Electric Co-op, Inc.	D	4,020	(503) 296-2740
West Oregon Electric Co-op, Inc.	D	3,678	(503) 429-3021

PENNSYLVANIA

Name of Cooperative	Type*	Consumer Members	Phone Number
Adams Electric Co-op, Inc.	D	23,006	(717) 334-9211
Allegheny Electric Co-op	GT		(717) 233-5704
Bedford REC, Inc.	D	7,915	(814) 623-5101
Central Electric Co-op, Inc.	D	22,108	(412) 399-2931
Claverack Rural Electric Co-op	D	15,655	(717) 265-2167
New Enterprise REC	D	3,006	(814) 766-3221
Northwestern RECA, Inc.	D	16,734	(814) 398-4651
Pennsylvania Rural Electric Assn.	S		(717) 233-5704
Somerset REC, Inc.	D	11,278	(814) 445-4106
Southwest Central RECC	D	19,845	(412) 349-4800
Sullivan County REC, Inc.	D	4,989	(717) 924-3381
Tri-County REC, Inc.	D	16,254	(717) 662-2175
United Electric Cooperative, Inc.	D	16,270	(814) 371-8570
Valley REC, Inc.	D	17,736	(814) 643-2650
Warren Electric Co-op, Inc.	D	8,525	(814) 563-7548

SOUTH CAROLINA

Name of Cooperative	Type*	Consumer Members	Phone Number
Aiken Electric Co-op, Inc.	D	31,294	(803) 649-6245
Berkeley Electric Co-op, Inc.	D	53,362	(803) 761-8200
Black River Electric Co-op, Inc.	D	21,808	(803) 469-8060
Blue Ridge Electric Co-op, Inc.	D	43,270	(803) 878-6326
Broad River Electric Co-op, Inc.	D	13,545	(803) 489-5737
Central Electric Power Co-op, Inc.	GT		(803) 779-4975
Co-op Electric Energy Supply	O		(803) 822-8100

*See page 226 for Key

Name of Cooperative	Type*	Consumer Members	Phone Number
Coastal Electric Co-op, Inc.	D	8,470	(803) 549-9512
Edisto Electric Co-op, Inc.	D	14,881	(803) 245-5141
Electric Cooperatives of S.C., Inc.	S		(803) 796-6060
Fairfield Electric Co-op, Inc.	D	15,362	(803) 635-4621
Horry Electric Co-op, Inc.	D	28,824	(803) 248-2211
Laurens Electric Co-op, Inc.	D	30,362	(803) 682-3141
Little River Electric Co-op, Inc.	D	9,974	(803) 459-2141
Lynches River Electric Co-op, Inc.	D	15,827	(803) 672-6111
Marlboro Electric Co-op, Inc.	D	5,310	(803) 479-3855
Mid-Carolina Electric Co-op, Inc.	D	34,186	(803) 359-5551
Newberry Electric Co-op, Inc.	D	9,382	(803) 276-1121
Palmetto Economic Development Corp.	O		(803) 254-9211
Palmetto Electric Co-op, Inc.	D	35,947	(803) 681-5551
Pee Dee Electric Co-op, Inc.	D	22,588	(803) 665-4070
Saluda River Electric Co-op	GT		(803) 682-3169
Santee Electric Co-op, Inc.	D	34,799	(803) 354-6187
Tri-County Electric Co-op, Inc.	D	13,738	(803) 874-1215
York Electric Co-op, Inc.	D	21,725	(803) 684-4247

SOUTH DAKOTA

Name of Cooperative	Type*	Consumer Members	Phone Number
Black Hills Electric Co-op, Inc.	D	5,478	(605) 673-4461
Bon Homme Yankton Electric Assn.	D	2,787	(605) 463-2507
Butte Electric Co-op, Inc.	D	2,850	(605) 456-2494
Cam-Wal Electric Co-op, Inc.	D	2,109	(605) 649-7676
Charles Mix Electric Assn., Inc.	D	1,853	(605) 487-7321
Cherry-Todd Electric Co-op, Inc.	D	4,368	(605) 856-4416
Clay-Union Electric Corp.	D	3,043	(605) 624-2673
Codington-Clark Electric Co-op	D	2,618	(605) 886-5848
Dakota Energy Cooperative, Inc.	D	3,267	(605) 352-8591
Douglas Electric Co-op, Inc.	D	815	(605) 724-2323
East River Electric Power Co-op	GT		(605) 256-4536

*See page 226 for Key

continued on page 218

SOUTH DAKOTA *(continued)*

Name of Cooperative	Type*	Consumer Members	Phone Number
F.E.M. Electric Assn., Inc.	D	2,032	(605) 426-6891
Grand Electric Co-op, Inc.	D	4,159	(605) 244-5211
H-D Electric Co-op, Inc.	D	2,958	(605) 874-2171
Heartland Consumers Power District	GT		(605) 256-6536
Intercounty Electric Assn., Inc.	D	3,092	(605) 996-7516
Kingsbury Electric Co-op, Inc.	D	885	(605) 854-3522
Lacreek Electric Assn., Inc.	D	4,992	(605) 685-6581
Lake Region Electric Assn., Inc.	D	3,254	(605) 345-3379
Lincoln-Union Electric Co.	D	3,439	(605) 934-1961
McCook Electric Co-op, Inc.	D	1,366	(605) 425-2661
Missouri Basin System Group	O		(605) 332-3536
Moreau Grand Electric Co-op, Inc.	D	5,152	(605) 865-3511
Northern Electric Co-op, Inc.	D	3,721	(605) 225-0310
Oahe Electric Co-op, Inc.	D	1,960	(605) 962-6243
Rosebud Electric Co-op, Inc.	D	4,930	(605) 835-9624
Rushmore Electric Power Co-op, Inc.	GT		(605) 342-4579
Sioux Valley Empire Electric Assn.	D	13,302	(605) 534-3535
South Dakota REA	S		(605) 224-8823
Spink Electric Co-op, Inc.	D	1,383	(605) 472-0380
Tri-County Electric Assn., Inc.	D	3,163	(605) 942-7786
Turner-Hutchinson Electric Co-op	D	3,635	(605) 648-3619
Union County Electric Co-op, Inc.	D	1,179	(605) 356-3395
West Central Electric Co-op, Inc.	D	5,938	(605) 669-2472
West River Co-op Telephone Co.	O		(605) 244-5213
West River Electric Assn., Inc.	D	9,371	(605) 279-2135
Whetstone Valley Electric Co-op	D	2,862	(605) 432-5331

*See page 226 for Key

TENNESSEE

Name of Cooperative	Type*	Consumer Members	Phone Number
Appalachian Electric Co-op	D	31,125	(615) 475-2032
Caney Fork Electric Co-op, Inc.	D	23,926	(615) 473-3116
Chickasaw Electric Co-op	D	10,019	(901) 465-3591
Cumberland EMC	D	58,708	(615) 645-2481
Duck River EMC	D	48,963	(615) 684-4621
Electric Research & Mfg. Co-op Inc.	O		(901) 285-9121
Fayetteville Electric System	D	15,075	(615) 433-1522
Forked Deer Electric Co-op, Inc.	D	8,590	(901) 836-7508
Fort Loudoun Electric Co-op	D	20,057	(615) 442-2487
Gibson EMC	D	30,401	(901) 855-4740
Holston Electric Co-op, Inc.	D	22,365	(615) 272-8821
LaFollette Utilities	D	17,104	(615) 562-3316
Lawrenceburg Power System	O	15,422	(615) 762-7161
Meriwether Lewis Electric Co-op	D	28,011	(615) 729-3558
Middle Tennessee EMC	D	90,937	(615) 890-9762
Mountain Electric Co-op	D	25,705	(615) 727-9111
Pickwick Electric Co-op	D	16,722	(901) 645-3411
Plateau Electric Co-op	D	13,151	(615) 569-8591
Powell Valley Electric Co-op	D	22,758	(615) 626-5204
Sequachee Valley Electric Co-op	D	25,815	(615) 837-8605
Southwest Tennessee EMC	D	36,113	(901) 772-1322
Tennessee Electric Co-op Assn.	S		(615) 367-9284
Tennessee Valley Electric Co-op	D	16,045	(901) 925-4916
Tennessee Valley Public Power Assn.	O		(615) 756-6511
Tri-County EMC	D	41,383	(615) 666-2111
Upper Cumberland EMC	D	35,337	(615) 735-2940
Volunteer Electric Co-op	D	75,856	(615) 334-5722

*See page 226 for Key

TEXAS

Name of Cooperative	Type*	Consumer Members	Phone Number
B-K Electric Co-op, Inc.	D	4,849	(817) 888-3441
Bailey County Electric Co-op, Inc.	D	5,824	(806) 272-4504
Bandera Electric Co-op, Inc.	D	18,304	(210) 796-3741
Bartlett Electric Co-op, Inc.	D	5,544	(817) 527-3551
Belfalls Electric Co-op, Inc.	D	4,437	(817) 583-7955
Bluebonnet Electric Co-op, Inc.	D	48,140	(409) 542-3151
Bowie-Cass Electric Co-op, Inc.	D	28,369	(903) 846-2311
Brazos Electric Power Co-op, Inc.	GT		(817) 750-6500
Cap Rock Electric Co-op, Inc.	D	24,013	(915) 683-5422
Central Texas Electric Co-op, Inc.	D	22,018	(210) 997-2126
Cherokee County Elec. Co-op Assn.	D	13,795	(903) 683-2248
Coleman County Electric Co-op, Inc.	D	7,631	(915) 625-2128
Comanche County Elec. Co-op Assn.	D	14,787	(915) 356-2533
Concho Valley Electric Co-op, Inc.	D	8,967	(915) 655-6957
Cooke County Electric Co-op Assn.	D	10,095	(817) 759-2211
Deaf Smith Electric Co-op, Inc.	D	9,984	(806) 364-1166
Deep East Texas Elec. Co-op, Inc.	D	31,826	(409) 275-2314
Denton County Electric Co-op, Inc.	D	30,368	(817) 383-1671
DeWitt Electric Cooperative Inc.	D	6,229	(512) 275-2334
Dickens Electric Co-op, Inc.	D	4,881	(806) 271-3311
East Texas Electric Co-op	O, GT		(409) 560-9532
Erath County Electric Co-op Assn.	D	16,535	(817) 965-3153
Fannin County Electric Co-op, Inc.	D	5,535	(903) 583-2118
Farmers Electric Co-op, Inc.	D	23,432	(903) 455-1715
Fayette Electric Co-op, Inc.	D	9,469	(409) 968-3181
Fort Belknap Electric Co-op, Inc.	D	4,860	(817) 564-2343
Gate City Electric Co-op, Inc.	D	1,780	(817) 937-2565
Golden Spread Electric Cooperative	GT		(806) 379-7766
Grayson-Collin Electric Co-op, Inc.	D	14,327	(903) 482-5231

*See page 226 for Key

Name of Cooperative	Type*	Consumer Members	Phone Number
Greenbelt Electric Co-op, Inc.	D	3,753	(806) 447-2536
Guadalupe Valley Elec. Co-op, Inc.	D	31,068	(210) 672-2871
Hamilton County Elec. Co-op Assn.	D	10,968	(817) 386-3123
Hereford Texas Federal Credit Union	O		(806) 364-1888
Hill County Electric Co-op, Inc.	D	12,466	(817) 687-2331
Houston County Electric Co-op, Inc.	D	14,973	(409) 544-5641
J.A.C. Electric Co-op Inc.	D	4,211	(817) 895-3311
Jackson Electric Co-op, Inc.	D	11,639	(512) 782-7193
Jasper-Newton Electric Co-op, Inc.	D	17,725	(409) 423-2241
Johnson County Electric Co-op Assn.	D	28,187	(817) 556-4000
Karnes Electric Co-op, Inc.	D	11,645	(210) 780-3952
Kaufman County Electric Co-op, Inc.	D	21,844	(214) 932-2214
Kimble Electric Co-op, Inc.	D	3,968	(915) 446-2625
L.C.R.A. Credit Union	O		(512) 474-1562
Lamar County Electric Co-op Assn.	D	8,526	(903) 784-4303
Lamb County Electric Co-op, Inc.	D	7,070	(806) 385-5191
Lighthouse Electric Co-op, Inc.	D	6,601	(806) 983-2814
Lower Colorado River Authority	GT		(512) 473-3200
Lyntegar Electric Co-op, Inc.	D	16,076	(806) 998-4588
Magic Valley Electric Co-op, Inc.	D	43,053	(210) 565-2451
McCulloch Electric Co-op, Inc.	D	4,977	(915) 597-2161
McLennan County Electric Co-op	D	8,019	(817) 840-2871
Medina Electric Co-op, Inc.	D	19,048	(210) 741-4384
Mid-South Electric Co-op Assn.	D	14,402	(409) 825-5100
Midwest Electric Co-op, Inc.	D	5,640	(915) 776-2244
Navarro County Electric Co-op, Inc.	D	8,732	(903) 874-7411
Navasota Valley Electric Co-op	D	12,458	(409) 828-3232
New Era Electric Co-op, Inc.	D	19,483	(903) 675-5688
North Plains Electric Co-op, Inc.	D	4,906	(806) 435-5482
Northeast Texas Elec. Co-op	GT		(903) 757-3282
Nueces Electric Co-op, Inc.	D	10,091	(512) 387-2581

*See page 226 for Key

continued on page 222

TEXAS *(continued)*

Name of Cooperative	Type*	Consumer Members	Phone Number
Panola-Harrison Electric Co-op	D	14,773	(903) 935-7936
Pedernales Electric Co-op, Inc.	D	94,277	(210) 868-7155
Rayburn County Electric Co-op	GT		(214) 722-1336
Rio Grande Electric Co-op, Inc.	D	8,631	(210) 563-2444
Rita Blanca Electric Co-op, Inc.	D	4,767	(806) 249-4506
Rusk County Electric Co-op, Inc.	D	15,562	(903) 657-4571
Sam Houston Electric Co-op, Inc.	D	50,392	(409) 327-5711
Sam Rayburn G&T, Inc.	GT		(409) 560-9532
San Bernard Electric Co-op, Inc.	D	14,567	(409) 865-3171
San Miguel Electric Co-op, Inc.	GT		(210) 784-3411
San Patricio Electric Co-op, Inc.	D	9,165	(512) 364-2220
South Plains Electric Co-op, Inc.	D	25,194	(806) 741-4200
South Texas Electric Co-op	GT		(512) 575-6491
Southwest Texas Elec. Co-op, Inc.	D	7,786	(915) 853-2544
Stamford Electric Co-op, Inc.	D	5,901	(915) 773-3684
Swisher Electric Co-op, Inc.	D	6,766	(806) 995-3567
Taylor Electric Co-op, Inc.	D	11,658	(915) 928-4715
Tex-La Electric Co-op of Texas	GT		(409) 560-9532
Texas Electric Cooperatives, Inc.	S		(512) 454-0311
Tri-County Electric Co-op, Inc.	D	31,361	(817) 444-3201
Upshur RECC	D	30,702	(903) 843-2536
Victoria Electric Co-op, Inc.	D	14,661	(512) 573-2428
Wharton County Electric Co-op, Inc.	D	4,870	(409) 543-6271
Wise Electric Co-op, Inc.	D	11,907	(817) 627-2167
Wood County Electric Co-op, Inc.	D	22,525	(903) 763-2203

UTAH

Name of Cooperative	Type*	Consumer Members	Phone Number
Deseret G&T Cooperative	GT		(801) 566-1238
Dixie-Escalante Rural Elec. Assn.	D	4,681	(801) 439-5311

*See page 226 for Key

Name of Cooperative	Type*	Consumer Members	Phone Number
Flowell Electric Association, Inc.	D	359	(801) 743-6214
GarKane Power Association, Inc.	D	6,753	(801) 896-5403
Intermountain Consumer Power	GT		(801) 566-3933
Intermountain Power Agency	O		(801) 262-8807
Moon Lake Electric Assn., Inc.	D	12,291	(801) 722-2448
Utah Rural Electric Association	S		(801) 566-3933

VERMONT

Hardwick Electric Department	D	3,696	(802) 472-5201
Vermont Electric Co-op, Inc.	D	13,855	(802) 635-2331
Vermont Electric G&T Cooperative	GT		(802) 635-2331
Vermont Public Power Supply Auth.	O		(802) 244-7678
Washington Electric Co-op, Inc.	D	8,259	(802) 223-5245

VIRGINIA

A & N Electric Cooperative	D	9,712	(804) 665-5116
BARC Electric Cooperative	D	10,056	(703) 997-9124
Central Virginia Electric Co-op	D	23,291	(804) 263-8336
Community Electric Co-op	D	8,422	(804) 242-6181
Craig-Botetourt Electric Co-op	D	5,470	(703) 864-5121
Mecklenburg Electric Co-op	D	25,976	(804) 372-6100
Nat'l. Society of Accountants	O		(703) 569-3088
Northern Neck Electric Co-op	D	13,779	(804) 333-3621
Northern Virginia Electric Co-op	D	75,999	(703) 335-0500
NRTC	O		(703) 787-0874
NRUCFC	O		(703) 709-6700
Old Dominion Electric Co-op	GT		(804) 747-0592
Prince George Electric Co-op	D	7,564	(804) 834-2424
Rappahannock Electric Co-op	D	60,067	(703) 898-8500
Shenandoah Valley Elec. Co-op, Inc.	D	27,966	(703) 434-2200

*See page 226 for Key

continued on page 224

VIRGINIA *(continued)*

Name of Cooperative	Type*	Consumer Members	Phone Number
Southside Electric Co-op	D	37,361	(804) 645-7721
Va., Md. & Del. Assn. of Elec Co-op	S		(804) 346-3344

WASHINGTON

Name of Cooperative	Type*	Consumer Members	Phone Number
Benton REA	D	10,218	(509) 786-2913
Big Bend Electric Co-op, Inc.	D	6,573	(509) 659-1700
C.A.R.E.S.	GT		(206) 750-7710
Columbia REA, Inc.	D	2,767	(509) 382-2578
Elmhurst Mutual Power & Light Co.	D	10,792	(206) 531-4646
Horizon Credit Union	O		(509) 928-6494
Inland Power & Light Company	D	23,235	(509) 747-7151
Lincoln Electric Co-op, Inc.	D	2,016	(509) 725-1141
Nespelem Valley Elec. Co-op	D	1,379	(509) 634-4571
Northwest PPA, Inc.	O		(360) 254-0109
OHOP Mutual Light Company	D	2,719	(206) 847-4364
Okanogan County Elec. Co-op	D	1,948	(509) 996-2228
Orcas Power & Light Company	D	9,166	(206) 376-3500
Parkland Light & Water Company	D	3,573	(206) 531-5666
Peninsula Light Company	D	21,875	(206) 857-5950
PUD No. 1 of Ferry County	D	2,664	(509) 775-3325
PUD No. 1 of Kittitas County	D	2,265	(509) 925-3164
PUD No. 1 of Klickitat County	O	8,810	(509) 773-5891
Tanner Electric	D	2,555	(206) 888-0623
Washington P.U.D. Association	O		(206) 682-3110
Washington RECA	S		(206) 357-6048

WEST VIRGINIA

Name of Cooperative	Type*	Consumer Members	Phone Number
Harrison REA, Inc.	D	5,030	(304) 624-6365

*See page 226 for Key

WISCONSIN

Name of Cooperative	Type*	Consumer Members	Phone Number
Adams-Columbia Electric Co-op	D	27,307	(608) 339-3346
Barron Electric Cooperative	D	13,012	(715) 537-3171
Bayfield Electric Co-op, Inc.	D	6,436	(715) 372-4287
Buffalo Electric Cooperative	D	3,644	(608) 685-4440
Central Wisconsin Electric Co-op	D	6,208	(715) 445-2211
Chippewa Valley Electric Co-op	D	5,450	(715) 239-6800
Clark Electric Co-op	D	7,147	(715) 267-6188
Crawford Electric Co-op	D	3,194	(608) 735-4313
Dairyland Power Co-op	GT		(608) 788-4000
Dunn County Electric Co-op	D	6,466	(715) 232-6240
Eau Claire Electric Co-op	D	7,951	(715) 832-1603
Grant-Lafayette Electric Co-op	D	7,403	(608) 723-2121
Head of the Lakes Electric Co-op	D	4,343	(715) 399-2212
Jackson Electric Co-op	D	5,261	(715) 284-5385
Jump River Electric Co-op	D	6,852	(715) 532-5524
Oakdale Electric Co-op	D	11,637	(608) 372-4131
Oconto Electric Co-op	D	7,004	(414) 846-2816
Pierce-Pepin Electric Co-op	D	5,307	(715) 273-4355
Polk-Burnett Electric Co-op	D	14,440	(715) 646-2191
Price Electric Co-op, Inc.	D	6,953	(715) 339-2155
Richland Electric Co-op	D	3,061	(608) 647-3173
Rock County Electric Co-op Assn.	D	4,616	(608) 752-4550
Rural Electric Supply Co-op	O		(608) 831-2600
St. Croix Electric Co-op	D	5,444	(715) 684-3336
Taylor Electric Cooperative	D	3,403	(715) 678-2411
Trempealeau Electric Co-op	D	8,134	(608) 323-3381
Vernon Electric Co-op	D	8,172	(608) 634-3121
Washington Island Elec. Co-op, Inc.	D	875	(414) 847-2541

*See page 226 for Key

WISCONSIN *(continued)*

Name of Cooperative	Type*	Consumer Members	Phone Number
Western Wisc. Communications Co-op	O		(715) 985-3004
Wisconsin Electric Co-op Assn.	S		(608) 273-0420

WYOMING

Name of Cooperative	Type*	Consumer Members	Phone Number
Big Horn REC	D	2,912	(307) 568-2419
Bridger Valley Electric Assn., Inc.	D	4,537	(307) 786-2800
Carbon Power & Light, Inc.	D	4,526	(307) 326-5206
Garland Light & Power Co.	D	1,257	(307) 754-2881
Hot Springs REA, Inc.	D	3,060	(307) 864-3157
Lower Valley Power & Light, Inc.	D	15,308	(307) 886-3175
Niobrara Electric Assn., Inc.	D	2,311	(307) 334-3221
Riverton Valley Electric Assn.	D	6,571	(307) 856-9426
Rural Electric Company, Inc.	D	6,083	(307) 245-3261
Sheridan-Johnson REA	D	2,114	(307) 674-6466
Tri-County Electric Assn., Inc.	D	15,386	(307) 283-3531
Wheatland REA	D	2,988	(307) 322-2125
Wyoming Rural Electric Assn.	S		(307) 234-6152
Wyrulec Company	D	3,738	(307) 837-2225

AMERICAN SAMOA

American Samoa Power Authority	D	8,758	(684) 644-5251

KEY

Type*

D = Distribution System

GT = Generation & Transmission Co-op

S = Statewide Organizations

O = Other

SUBJECT INDEX